The Essential TI-108 Activity Book

DAVID E. WILLIAMS, Ed.D.

STOKES PUBLISHING COMPANY

Sunnyvale, California

**To Ozzie, my late brother,
who saw a teacher in me.**

www.stokespublishing.com

©1992 by Stokes Publishing Company
1292 Reamwood Avenue
Sunnyvale, California 94089

Printed in the United States of America
Seventh printing, 2011

ISBN 0-914534-08-4

CONTENTS

Activity Sheets and Lesson Helpers

ABOUT THE BOOK

Texas Instrument's TI-108 is the most popular basic calculator used in classrooms today. Since it first came on the market, it has been used by thousands of teachers at every level of instruction, from elementary schools to high schools. Though labeled a basic four-function calculator, it can become a very powerful calculator in the hands of a skilled user.

The Essential TI-108 Activity Book has been written to provide teachers who use this popular calculator with a source book, in order to take full advantage of the TI-108 as an effective tool and instructional aid in teaching mental math, estimation, number sense, and problem solving.

Because the TI-108 is used at so many grade levels, this source book contains activities that span the grades, from number-numeral recognition skills taught at the primary level to pre-algebra skills taught in the middle grades. Thus the word "Essential" in the title; if you use the TI-108, then this book is for you.

Teachers are eager to implement the recommendations involving technology, specifically calculators, contained in the National Council of Teachers of Mathematics' *Curriculum and Evaluation Standards for School Mathematics*. This book contains the needed material for teachers to effectively use the TI-108 with their students.

The Essential TI-108 Activity Book features the following sections:

Teacher Workshop

This section contains instruction for teachers to learn how to use the TI-108; it will take teachers through the features and keys of the TI-108 with easy-to-follow instructions. It is designed for teachers to read with TI-108 in hand. Practice sets will provide teachers with examples so that they will gain the needed confidence to integrate the use of calculators into their mathematics instruction.

Topics and Ideas

This section contains suggestions for teachers to integrate calculator use in the mathematics curriculum. Teachers can use the TI-108 as students develop basic mathematic skills and concepts and engage in problem solving.

Activity Sheets and Lesson Helpers

This section contains lessons for using the TI-108 in mathematics instruction. It includes a feature called "lesson helpers" with accompanying activity sheets. The "lesson helpers" include objectives, detailed procedures, answers, and extensions for easy use. Many additional ideas will be included in this section to help teachers use the TI-108 as a valuable instructional aid in teaching problem solving, estimation, number sense, and mental math.

The Essential TI-108 Activity Book contains suggestions for using The Educator‑ Basic Overhead‑ calculator developed by Stokes Publishing Company. It matches the keyboard and display of the TI-108 and can be used with any overhead projector. It is a valuable aid to use with students as they learn to operate the TI-108.

Use this book to help students discover and explore mathematics with the TI-108.

TEACHER'S TI-108 WORKSHOP

This section of *The Essential TI-108 Activity Book* is for you, the teacher. It is not for your students. You will use the knowledge you gain from working through this section when teaching your students how to use their TI-108 calculators.

As you read this section, have a TI-108 in hand. Use it to do all the exercises. This is the best way to learn how to use a TI-108 and then use it effectively when teaching students. Answers to all the exercise sets appear at the end of the section.

When working with your students, you may need to refer back to parts of this section and review a feature of the TI-108.

[ON/C]

This is a dual-function key. It turns the calculator on when its solar panel is exposed to light. It also performs a clearing function; the display, any constants that are in effect, and any operation that is pending are cleared.

But let's not get ahead of ourselves. Slide the top of the case off the calculator and insert the TI-108 in the top. Sometimes when the calculator is exposed to light, the display contains bits and pieces of digits. The electronic digits are all made from an 8. You may see different parts of the segments of an electronic 8 in the display. Press [ON/C]. A 0 will appear in the display; you are now ready for action. We will return to this key shortly.

Number Keys and [=]

Numbers are keyed into the calculator just as you would write them with pencil and paper. For **12**, you would write the the tens' digit **1** first followed by the units' digit **2**. Do it the same way on your calculator. Press the **1** key followed by the **2** key. The number **12** is displayed. Press [ON/C].

For **123**, press the **1** key then the **2** key, then **3**. Press [ON/C].

For **321**, press **3**, then **2**, then **1**. For decimal numbers, press the decimal point key exactly as if you were writing the decimal number.

SET I
Key in each number, then press [ON/C].

1. 25	**2.** 258
3. 852	**4.** 1762
5. 2671	**6.** 1.5
7. 0.004	**8.** 2 1.12
9. 1,000,674	**10.** 271.046

Press [3] [+] [4] [=].

The display reads 7. The [=] key is important. It processes whatever operation or operations that are pending and automatically prepares the calculator for the next computation. In other words, you do not have to clear the display between computations.

Press [5] [−] [2] [=].

See, you did not have to clear the **7** before pressing the **5**. Keep going, [8] [x] [4] [=]. [2] [8] [÷] [7] [=].

The displays read 3, 32, and 4 respectively each time you pressed the [=] key.

On some of the activity sheets in this book, it is recommended that with primary students you do clear the display between computations so these students begin each time with a display of 0; otherwise, they may become confused with seeing a non-zero number in the display, the result of the previous calculation.

SET II
Compute

1. 27 x 32	**2.** 354 + 639 + 277
3. 985 − 438 + 216	**4.** 3,861 ÷ 27

[ON/C]

In addition to using this key when you first turn on the calculator, it can also be used to clear an incorrect number entry and also to clear the display.

Press [6] [+] [3] and stop with the 3 in the display.

Let's suppose a mistake has been made, that **5** is to be added to **6**. Press [ON/C] one time. The **3** is "erased." Press [5] [=] and the display shows 11, the sum of **6** and **5**.

So, pressing ON/C one time after a number entry will clear the displayed number.

Now press this sequence: 6 + 3 ON/C ON/C 5 =.

Your display reads 5 because pressing the ON/C key twice clears the display. So, if you want to be sure you are "starting from scratch," press this key twice. Clearing the display using the ON/C key has no effect on the contents of memory.

SET III
Guess the displays for each of the following, then use your TI-108 to verify your guesses.

1. 1 8 − 7 ON/C 1 0 =
2. 6 ON/C 5 + 7 ON/C 4 =
3. 8 X 5 + 9 ON/C 2 =
4. 8 X 5 + 9 ON/C ON/C 2 + 4 =

The ON/C key is also used to clear errors. Key in the largest possible number. That gives you a display with a 9 in each of the places. The TI-108 is referred to as an **eight-digit display calculator** because that's the most digits you can fit in the display. Let's try to add **1** to **99,999,999**.

Press + 1 =.

Your display reads 1.0000000 or 1. with an **E** in the lower left-hand corner of the display. This is the error indicator; it's telling you that you overflowed the display. Try to key in a number. You can't. The display is frozen in the error mode. To get a 0 in the display, press ON/C twice.

SET IV
Each of these sequences will yield an error message. Key in each sequence, then clear each error.

1. 87,235,988 + 22,635,108   2. 6 + 0
3. 475,000 x 34,876   4. 760,000 + 0.00045

Logic System

The TI-108 has a logic system which processes operations from left to right regardless of the standard order of operations.

Using mental math, what is the value of **2 x 3 + 5**? The correct answer is **11**. Using any calculator, you will get a display of 11.

Key in 2 X 3 + 5 =.

Now, **5 + 2 x 3** is also **11**.

Key in 5 + 2 X 3 =.

The TI-108 yields a display of **21**, an incorrect answer. The calculator works from left to right and adds the **2** to the **5** for a sum of **7**, and then multiplies **3** by **7** for a product of **21**.

When students use the TI-108 to do involved calcula-

tions including combinations of all four operations, they must use the memory keys.

TI-108 users utilize mental-math strategies and knowledge of operations to simplify many computations for direct entry.

Simplify **4 + 7 x 5**. Think: **4 + 7 x 5 = 7 x 5 + 4**.
Press 7 X 5 + 4 =.
The display reads 39.

Simplify **(9 x 2 + 5) x 3**. The = key can be used to "close off" a set of parantheses.
Press 9 X 2 + 5 = X 3 =.
The display reads 69.

Simplify **24 x (17 − 9)**. Think: **17 − 9 = 8**.
Press 2 4 X 8 =.
The display reads 192.

SET V
Compute.

1. 5 x 6 + 2   2. 2 + 5 x 6
3. 30 + 5 x 2 + 4   4. 30 + (5 x 2) + 4
5. 5 x 7 + 3 x 6   6. 5 x (7 + 3 x 6)
7. 18 − 7 x 2   8. 2 + 4 x (3 x 3 + 5)
9. (3 + 5) x (7 − 4) 10. 2 x 17 + 4 − 5
11. (3 + 5 x 9) + 16   12. 2 x (17 + 8 + 4)

Constant Operations

The TI-108 calculator has constant capability for all four operations. This means you can add, subtract, multiply, or divide by the same number.

For addition

Press	Display
0 + 3 =	3
=	6
=	9
=	12

Notice that when the first = key is pressed, the display reads 3 (0 + 3). Each time the = key is pressed, 3 is added to the previous display. Addition by 3 is stored and automatically added each time the = key is pressed.

For subtraction

Press	Display
8 − 2 =	6
=	4
=	2
=	0

The first display reads 6 (8 − 2). Each time the = key is pressed, the second number in the original subtraction is constantly subtracted from the previous display, 4 (6 − 2), 2 (4 − 2), and 0 (2 − 2). Subtraction by 2 is stored and automatically subtracted each time the = key is pressed.

For multiplication

Press	Display
2 × 4 =	8
=	16
=	32
=	64

Fooled you, didn't we? The first display reads **8 (2 x 4)**. Each time the = key is pressed, the first number in the original multiplication is constantly multiplied by the previous display, **16 (2 x 8)**, **32 (2 x 16)**, and **64 (2 x 32)**. Multiplication by 2 is stored and automatically used each time the = key is pressed. It makes sense here that it's the first number or factor used as the constant. Recall, **3 x 4** as repeated addition is **4 + 4 + 4**.

For division

Press	Display
2 5 6 ÷ 4 =	64
=	16
=	4
=	1

Division by **4** is "remembered" each time the = key is pressed. Each previous display is divided by **4**.

Show the results of adding **6** to **4**, **7**, **3**, **8**, and **2**, respectively.
Press: 4 + 6 = 7 = 3 = 8 = 2 =
The displays each time the = key is pressed read 10, 13, 9, 14, and 8.

Show the results of subtracting **5** from **17**, **20**, **9**, **5**, and **11**.
Press: 1 7 − 5 = 2 0 = 9 = 5 = 1 1 =
The displays each time the = key is pressed read 12, 15, 4, 0, and 6.

Show the results of multiplying **2**, **8**, **12**, **5**, and **7** by **3**.
Press: 3 × 2 = 8 = 1 2 = 5 = 7 =
The displays each time the = key is pressed read 6, 24, 36, 15, and 21.

Show the results of dividing **24**, **18**, **30**, **12**, and **60** by **6**.
Press: 2 4 ÷ 6 = 1 8 = 3 0 = 1 2 = 6 0 =
The displays each time the = key is pressed read 4, 3, 5, 2, and 10.

SET VI

Guess the displays each time the = key is pressed, then use your TI-108 to verify your guesses.

1. 1 + 1 = = = = = = = =
2. 7 × 4 = 3 = 8 = 2 =
3. 1 0 − 2 = = = = =
4. 1 0 + 2 = 5 = 1 3 = 1 7 = 6 =
5. 2 5 ÷ 5 = 7 5 = 3 0 = 4 5 = 2 0 =
6. 2 × 1 = = = = = =
7. 5 0 − 5 = = = = = =
8. 4 ÷ 2 = = = =

A "new" calculation involving a different operation and two numbers will clear a constant that has been in effect. Pressing ON/C will also clear a constant.

Memory Keys

Using your TI-108, you can store numbers in memory for later use. The ability to store numbers in memory is useful in many applications, especially with the TI-108 not processing operations according to the standard order of operations.

Press 2 + 3 =.
The display reads 5. Assume you want to save the 5.

Press M+.
Pressing M+ adds the displayed number **(5)** to the number that is in memory **(0 + 5)**. The TI-108 has a **memory indicator**, telling you that you saved something. An **M** appears in the upper left-hand corner of the display.

Press ON/C.
A 0 is now in the display, but the memory indicator is still in the display.

Press MRC.
There's the **5**. Pressing MRC one time does the "R" in "MRC," it recalls memory to the display.

Press MRC.
Pressing this key twice does the "C" in "MRC," it clears the memory. The **5** has been brought to the display but the memory is now cleared. Notice that the memory indicator is no longer in the display.

Press 4 M+ M+ M+.
Each time the M+ key is pressed, **4** is added to the memory. How much are three 4's?

Press MRC.
There's the **12**.

Press 7 M−.
Pressing M− subtracts the number in the display from the number in the memory. What is **12 − 7**?

Press MRC.
There's the **5**.

When you are doing a series of calculations that involve the use of the memory keys, you want to clear the memory before starting the next problem. Otherwise, you will get an error buildup in the memory. If the memory indicator is not present in the display, then the memory is clear. When the MRC key is pressed twice, the contents of memory are brought to the active display. With young students, you may now want to press the ON/C key so a 0 appears in the display.

Compute **2 x 3 + 4 x 5**.
With or without parentheses, this expression is interpreted as the sum of the products of **2 x 3** and **4 x 5**. The TI-108 will not provide a display of 26 if the sequence is keyed in directly. Proper use of memory keys will solve this problem.

Press $\boxed{2}\boxed{\times}\boxed{3}\boxed{=}\boxed{M+}\boxed{4}\boxed{\times}\boxed{5}\boxed{=}\boxed{M+}\boxed{MRC}$.
Both products were computed, then saved. The result of adding the two products is in the memory, so pressing $\boxed{MRC}$ gives you **26**. Another way...

Press $\boxed{MRC}\boxed{ON/C}\boxed{2}\boxed{\times}\boxed{3}\boxed{=}\boxed{M+}\boxed{4}\boxed{\times}\boxed{5}\boxed{+}\boxed{MRC}\boxed{=}$.
In the former example, the products were summed in memory, then recalled. In this example, the first product is stored. The sum of the two products is performed in the display when the first product is recalled and added to the second product.

If you understand the above procedures involving single-digit numbers, then you can use the memory keys to do more involved problems.

SET VII
Do the following using the memory keys.

1. 27 x 45 + 65 x 23   2. 12 x 18 – 11 x 13 + 16 x 19
3. How much: two items @ $1.87, 3 items @ 2.49, and 1 item @ 4.19?
4. Mary bought 2 loaves of bread @ 89 cents each and 3 cans of juice @ $1.05 each. How much change from a $5 bill?

Change Key Sign
The TI-108 has a change sign key $\boxed{+/-}$. It is useful when working with integers. When pressed, it will display the opposite or the additive inverse of the displayed number.

Press $\boxed{5}\boxed{+/-}$.
The number in the display was **5**. After pressing $\boxed{+/-}$, the display shows the opposite of **5**, **−5**. Notice that the negative sign is at the extreme left of the display.

Show **−4 x −5 = 20**.

Press $\boxed{4}\boxed{+/-}\boxed{\times}\boxed{5}\boxed{+/-}\boxed{=}$

SET VIII
Compute.

1. 7 + −6 + 4 + −9   2. 45 + −9
3. 12 − −4   4. −4 x 6 x −2

Square Root Key
To the right of the $\boxed{+/-}$ key on the keyboard is the square root key. When pressed, the display will show the positive square root of the number that was previously in the dis-

play. Recall that both the product of **−5 x −5** and **5 x 5** is **25**.

Press $\boxed{2}\boxed{5}\boxed{\sqrt{}}$.
The display will show 5.

Press $\boxed{1}\boxed{4}\boxed{4}\boxed{\sqrt{}}$.
The display will show 12.

Compute $\sqrt{6^2 + 8^2}$.

Press $\boxed{6}\boxed{\times}\boxed{=}\boxed{M+}\boxed{8}\boxed{\times}\boxed{=}\boxed{M+}\boxed{MRC}\boxed{\sqrt{}}$.
The display should read 10.

SET IX
Compute.

1. $\sqrt{81}$ 2. $\sqrt{1225}$
3. $\sqrt{9^2 + 12^2}$ 4. $\sqrt{9^2} + \sqrt{12^2}$

Percent Key
Also on the top row of the keyboard is the percent key. Using the TI-108 to find a percent of a number is not analogous to the traditional paper and pencil method.

Find **20% of 45**.
Press $\boxed{4}\boxed{5}\boxed{\times}\boxed{2}\boxed{0}\boxed{\%}$.
The display reads 9.

Find **87.5% of 80**.
Press $\boxed{8}\boxed{0}\boxed{\times}\boxed{8}\boxed{7}\boxed{.}\boxed{5}\boxed{\%}$.
The display reads 70.

SET X
Compute.

1. Find 40% of 75   2. Find 23% of 56
3. Find 1.5% of 28   4. Find 150% of 102

6 is **25%** of what number?
Press $\boxed{6}\boxed{\div}\boxed{2}\boxed{5}\boxed{\%}$.
The display reads 24.

18 is **150%** of what number?
Press $\boxed{1}\boxed{8}\boxed{\div}\boxed{1}\boxed{5}\boxed{0}\boxed{\%}$.
The display reads 12.

SET XI
Compute

1. 80% of what number is 16?
2. 15.4 is 5% of what number?
3. 23 is 8% of what number?
4. 125% of what number is 62.5?

ANSWERS TO PROBLEM SETS

SET I
Displays should be the same as the numbers that are keyed in; the objective here was to see if you cleared the display between entering the numbers.

SET II
1. 864   2. 1270   3. 763   4. 143

SET III
1. 8   2. 9   3. 42   4. 6

SET IV
Each display yielded an error message.

SET V
1. 32   2. 32   3. 16   4. 7   5. 53
6. 125   7. 4   8. 58   9. 24   10. 3.5
11. 3   12. 38

SET VI
1. 2, 3, 4, 5, 6, 7, 8   2. 28, 21, 56, 14
3. 8, 6, 4, 2, 0   4. 12, 7, 15, 19, 8
5. 5, 15, 6, 9, 4
6. 2, 4, 8, 16, 32, 64, 128
7. 45, 40, 35, 30, 25, 20
8. 2, 1, 0.5, 0.25

SET VII
1. 2710   2. 377   3. $15.40   4. $.07

SET VIII
1. −4   2. −5   3. 16   4. 48

SET IX
1. 9   2. 35   3. 15   4. 21

SET X
1. 30   2. 12.88   3. 0.42   4. 153

SET XI
1. 20   2. 308   3. 287.5   4. 50

TOPICS AND IDEAS

This book contains activities for use with the TI-108. The level of the activities spans the grades from kindergarten through middle school. As you work through your curriculum, you will find yourself picking and choosing an appropriate activity to use with your class. All of the features of the TI-108 are covered on various pages of this book.

Two major objectives of the material contained in *The Essential TI-108 Activity Book* are to help students become familiar with technology and to build their confidence in using calculators as they develop concepts about mathematics.

The purpose of this section is to provide you with topics and ideas to help you integrate calculators into your curriculum. Use the topics and ideas which follow to act as a springboard to creating your own calculator activities.

Number-Numeral Recognition

Use the TI-108 when students are beginning to use numerals to name numbers. An electronic 23 in a TI-108 display is another method of showing the numeral for twenty-three items.

Place Value

This is a fertile area for students to explore with their TI-108 calculators. At the primary level: "Use base ten blocks and model the number, '37.' Show on your TI-108." Show 67 on the Basic Overhead Calculator. Have students key in the number that is ten more, 2 tens less, etc. Students study place value as they proceed through the grades. As students study place value into six or more places, the use of the TI-108 will be a valuable aid.

Counting

The constant feature of the TI-108 provides opportunities for rich explorations of number patterns and for counting activities.

Count by 2's: [0][+][2][=][=][=] etc. Count by 2's beginning at 7: [7][+][2][=][=][=] etc. Count backwards from 50 by 3's: [5][0][-][3][=][=][=][=] etc. At the middle school level, the TI-108 gives students the power to explore patterns with decimals. Count by halves:

[0][+][.][5][=][=][=] etc. Count by halves beginning at 7: [7][+][.][5][=][=][=] etc. Count backwards from 999 by 10's: [9][9][9][-][1][0][=][=][=][=] etc. In this book, this feature is also used with multiplication and division. The automatic constant for multiplication allows you to explore exciting patterns with exponents.

Place Value

The use of the TI-108 aids the problem-solving process. In the primary grades, if students are finding two odd numbers with a sum of 37, the use of the calculator frees them from the computations involved and allows them to look for patterns. There are many activities in this book which focus on different aspects of problem solving. In later grades, computation is extended to all four operations with whole numbers, fractions, and decimals and this provides additional opportunities for more problem-solving experiences.

Estimation

Students cannot use a calculator effectively if they do not have good estimation skills. Estimation activities in the primary grades are limited because of the few computational skills studied to this point. Nevertheless, guess-and-verify activities can be used at this level. For the sum of 9 + 9 + 8 + 9, you want students to be able to estimate the sum as 40; determine the appropriateness of the estimate by using the TI-108. As computation is extended to all four operations with whole numbers and decimals, the use of the TI-108 is crucial in continuing to develop good estimation skills. For the product of 18.76 x 23.83, you want students to be able to estimate the product as 400 (20 x 20); determine the appropriateness of the estimate by using the TI-108. Various estimation strategies are used in this book.

Number Sense

It is in the primary grades where good number sense is developed. Calculator activities can help students gain an intuitive grasp about concepts like commutativity and associativity long before these properties are formally studied. Working with all four operations, the distributive property of multiplication over addition can be explored using calculators.

Mental Math

While it may seem like a contradiction, the TI-108 can be used to encourage mental math. One of the most important aspects of using calculators with young students is to show them that many computations can be done much faster mentally than with a calculator. You can shape students' appropriate use of the TI-108 by using flash cards, competitions, and timed drills to emphasize the importance of mental math. Effective use of calculators is based on mastery of basic skills. One of your major tasks is the development of basic skills; the use of calculators will not change this task.

Applications

Applying mathematics is a major goal of elementary mathematics. There are several consumer-oriented activities in this book. Once students learn all the features of the TI-108 calculator, it becomes a valuable tool in all application lessons.

Cooperative Learning

The use of calculators in a cooperative-learning environment is an effective instructional strategy. Many of the activities in this book lend themselves to a grouping of students.

The activities contained in the next section should not be thought of as worksheets. Examine the activity sheets closely. Notice the lack of directions; this is intended. They are designed for the teacher of elementary and middle school students to be used as he/she works with students to develop mathematics concepts with the use of the calculator. Answers to all problems are electronically imprinted on the activity sheets and will not print when you make copies of activity sheets.

Each activity has a corresponding lesson helper. The *Procedures for Use* and the *Extension* parts of the lesson helpers contain many helpful hints and suggestions for using the TI-108 with your students. The lesson helpers also contain suggested uses of the Basic Overhead Calculator as you use the TI-108 with your students.

WORD NAMES

	Number Name	Record Display

1. ON/C   Eleven   *11.*

2. ON/C   Eighty-three   *83.*

3. ON/C   One hundred, seventy-nine   *179.*

4. ON/C   Four hundred, seven   *407.*

5. ON/C   Eight hundred, twenty  *820.*

6. ON/C   Eight hundred, two  *802.*

7. ON/C   Six hundred, ten  *610.*

8. ON/C   Nine hundred, ninety-nine  *999.*

See Lesson Helper, page 67

Word Names • 1

KNOW YOUR PLACE (VALUE)

		Words	**Record Display**

1. ON/C 3 tens, 7 ones `37.`

2. ON/C 7 tens, 3 ones `73.`

3. ON/C 2 hundreds, 5 tens, 4 ones `254.`

4. ON/C 2 hundreds, 4 tens, 5 ones `245.`

5. ON/C 5 hundreds, 0 tens, 6 ones `506.`

6. ON/C 3 hundreds, 3 tens, 0 ones `330.`

7. ON/C 8 hundreds, 0 tens, 9 ones `809.`

8. ON/C 7 hundreds, 9 tens, 7 ones `797.`

WHAT'S THE COUNT?

How many?	Use your calculator	Record display

1. Key in number.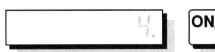

2. ▌▌▌▌▌ ▌▌▌ Key in number.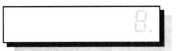

3. X X X X X
X X X X X Key in number.

4. ✳✳✳✳✳ ✳✳✳
✳✳✳✳✳ Key in number.

5. *0000000*
0000000 Key in number.

6. Key in number.

7. 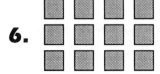 Key in number.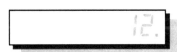

8. & & & & &
& & & & &
& & & & Key in number.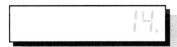

COUNT THE BUGS

Count the bugs. Key in the numbers to be added.

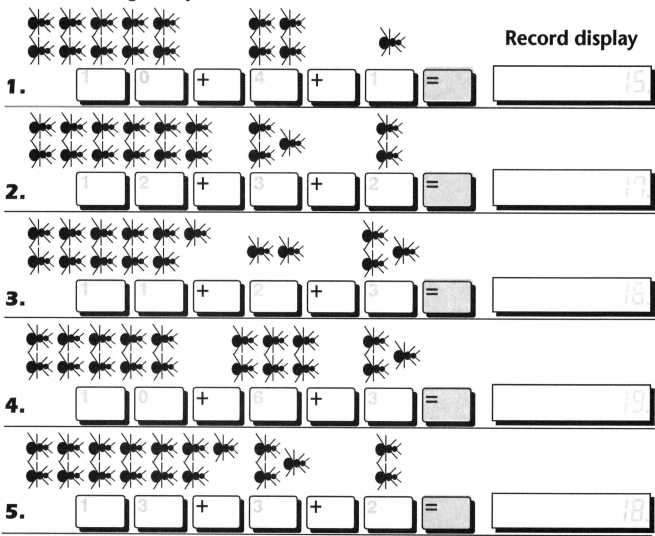

Record display

1. `1` `0` `+` `4` `+` `1` `=` | `15.`

2. `1` `2` `+` `3` `+` `2` `=` | `17.`

3. `1` `1` `+` `2` `+` `3` `=` | `16.`

4. `1` `0` `+` `6` `+` `3` `=` | `19.`

5. `1` `3` `+` `3` `+` `2` `=` | `18.`

Draw the number of bugs to match each sequence. Fill in each display.

6. `1` `3` `+` `4` `+` `2` `=` | `19.`

7. `1` `6` `+` `0` `+` `3` `=` | `19.`

TALLY TIME

Count each tally. Key in number. Record the displays.

Record your display.

1.

2.

3.

4.

5.

6.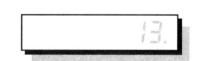

7.

8.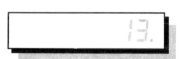

9.

10.

THE WAY HOME

Use your calculator. Help Mary take a number home.

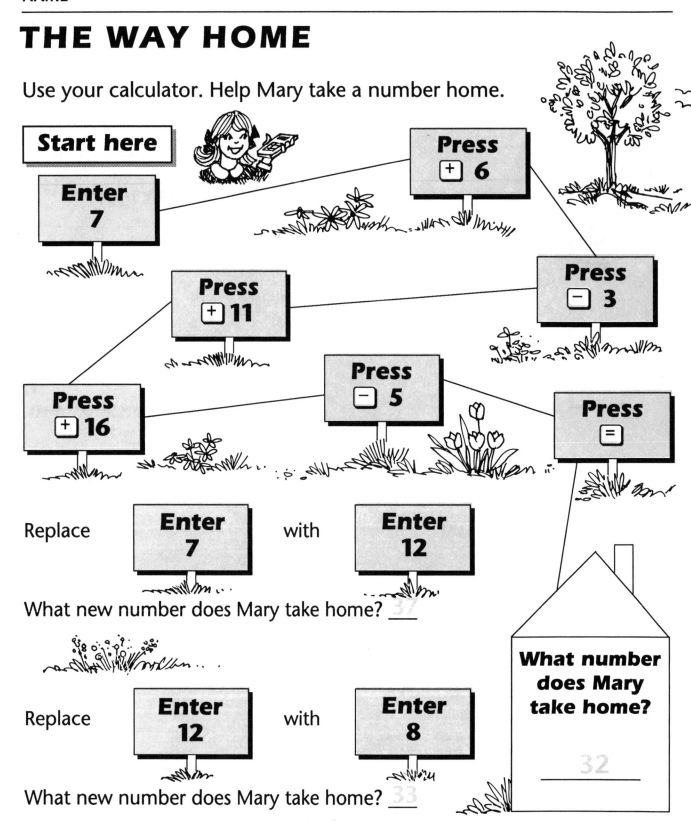

Replace **Enter 7** with **Enter 12**

What new number does Mary take home? 37

Replace **Enter 12** with **Enter 8**

What new number does Mary take home? 33

What number does Mary take home?

32

See Lesson Helper, page 69

CLEAR SAILING

Key in each sequence.

Copy final display

1. | 9 | + | 1 | 4 | = |

2. | 8 | + | 1 | 4 | ON/C |
| 1 | 2 | = |

3. | 5 | + | 3 | ON/C | 1 |
| + | 8 | = |

4. | 7 | ON/C | 5 | + | 3 |
| − | 4 | ON/C | 2 | = |

5. | 8 | + | 7 | ON/C | ON/C | 3 | = |

6. | 4 | ON/C | 7 | − | 2 |
| ON/C | 3 | + | 9 | = |

7. | 6 | + | 7 | ON/C | ON/C |
| 5 | − | 2 | = |

8. | 4 | ON/C | ON/C | 6 | + | 7 | = |

SNAKE THE SEQUENCES

Follow the sequence trails with your calculator.
Fill in the missing numbers.

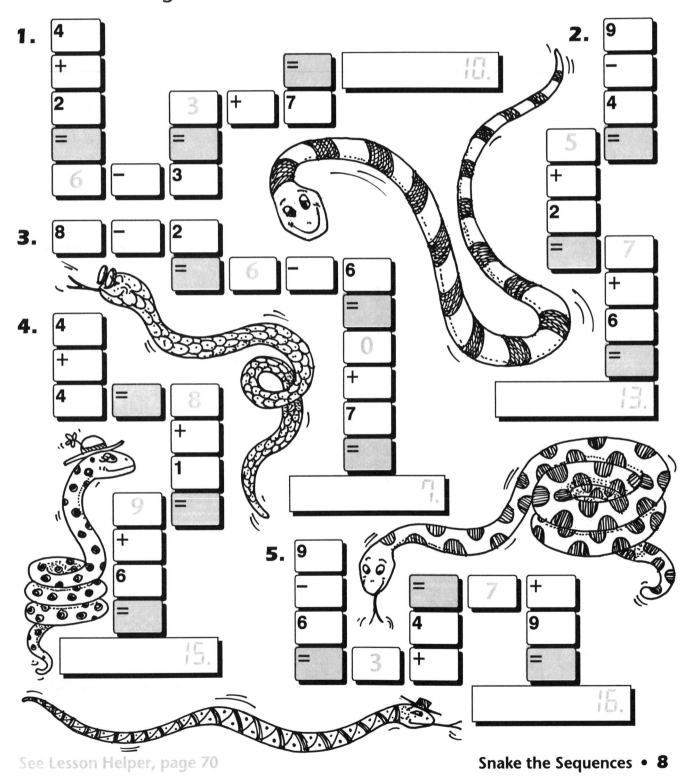

A DOG RIDDLE

Can you solve the riddle?

Find the missing number for each sequence.

Put the letter that matches each answer in the correct space below.

RIDDLE
What kind of dog likes cows?

1. [7] [+] [1] [5] [=]　22.
2. [1] [8] [−] [9] [=]　9.
3. [1] [1] [+] [1] [=]　12.
4. [5] [+] [1] [6] [=]　21.
5. [2] [7] [−] [8] [=]　19.
6. [8] [+] [1] [9] [=]　27.
7. [3] [0] [−] [5] [=]　25.
8. [4] [4] [−] [6] [=]　38.

8	19	16	6	11	5	7	9
L	D	L	G	U	O	A	B

A　B　U　L　L　D　O　G

1. ___ 2. ___ 3. ___ 4. ___ 5. ___ 6. ___ 7. ___ 8. ___

THE COVER-UP RIDDLE

What is Mary hiding?
Find out by using your calculator.
Place letters next to displays in the
spaces above the same numbers below.

1.  A

2.  E

3.  E

4.  S

5.  T

6.  K

7.  P

8.  N

Mary has a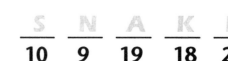

HARVEST THE NUMBERS

Complete the sequences.
Pick digits from the number tree.
All digits from the tree must be used.
As you pick digits, cross them out.

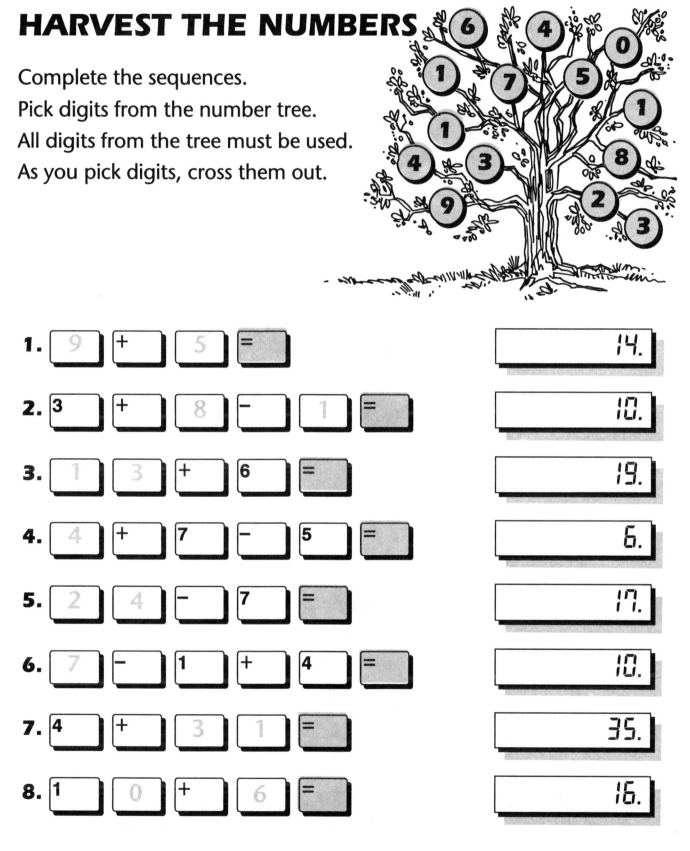

1. $\boxed{9} + \boxed{5} = $ ▨ $14.$

2. $\boxed{3} + \boxed{8} - \boxed{1} = $ ▨ $10.$

3. $\boxed{1 \quad 3} + \boxed{6} = $ ▨ $19.$

4. $\boxed{4} + \boxed{7} - \boxed{5} = $ ▨ $6.$

5. $\boxed{2 \quad 4} - \boxed{7} = $ ▨ $17.$

6. $\boxed{7} - \boxed{1} + \boxed{4} = $ ▨ $10.$

7. $\boxed{4} + \boxed{3 \quad 1} = $ ▨ $35.$

8. $\boxed{1 \quad 0} + \boxed{6} = $ ▨ $16.$

See Lesson Helper, page 71

COIN VALUES

How much?

Record your display.

1.

2.

3.

4.

5.

6.

7.

8.

See Lesson Helper, page 71

MORE COIN VALUES

How much?

1.   `0.31`

2.  `0.31`

3.   `0.86`

4.   `0.78`

5.   `1.05`

Now, try the next five problems by the numbers.

	Quarters	Dimes	Nickles	Pennies	
6.	2	3	1	2	`0.87`
7.	3	2	0	0	`0.95`
8.	4	0	0	0	`1.`
9.	5	1	3	0	`1.5`
10.	4	2	2	4	`1.34`

See Lesson Helper, page 71

More Coin Values • **13**

NAME

PRICE TAGS

Show each price tag in dollars and cents on your display.
Copy your displays.

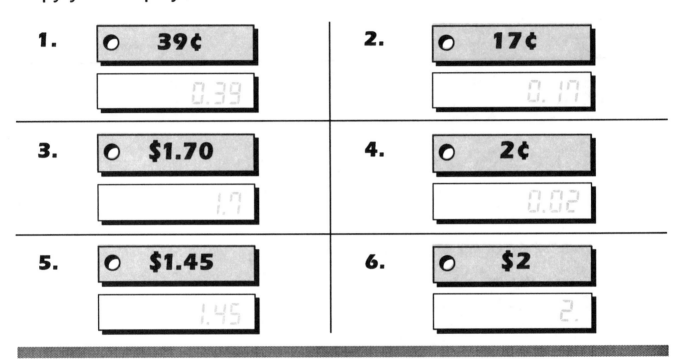

1. ⊙ **39¢**   0.39

2. ⊙ **17¢**   0.17

3. ⊙ **$1.70**   1.7

4. ⊙ **2¢**   0.02

5. ⊙ **$1.45**   1.45

6. ⊙ **$2**   2.

Each display shows a money answer.
Write up the price tag.

7. ⊙ 65¢   0.65

8. ⊙ $1.37   1.37

9. ⊙ $6.50   6.5

10. ⊙ 40¢   0.4

11. ⊙ 6¢   0.06

12. ⊙ $4   4.

See Lesson Helper, page 72

Price Tags • 14

OPERATION FILL IN

Each sequence is missing two operations.
Find the missing operations.

Where are the "+"
and "–" signs?

1. [2] [ ] [1] [ ] [6] [=]   9.

2. [7] [ ] [2] [ ] [3] [=]   6.

3. [8] [ ] [3] [ ] [3] [=]   14.

4. [8] [+ or –] [3] [– or +] [3] [=]   8.

5. [7] [ ] [2] [ ] [2] [=]   3.

6. [1] [2] [ ] [7] [ ] [3] [=]   8.

7. [7] [ ] [1] [2] [ ] [4] [=]   15.

8. [1] [2] [ ] [7] [ ] [8] [=]   11.

9. [8] [+ or –] [8] [– or +] [8] [=]   8.

10. [6] [ ] [2] [ ] [8] [=]   0.

See Lesson Helper, page 72

STICK SUMS

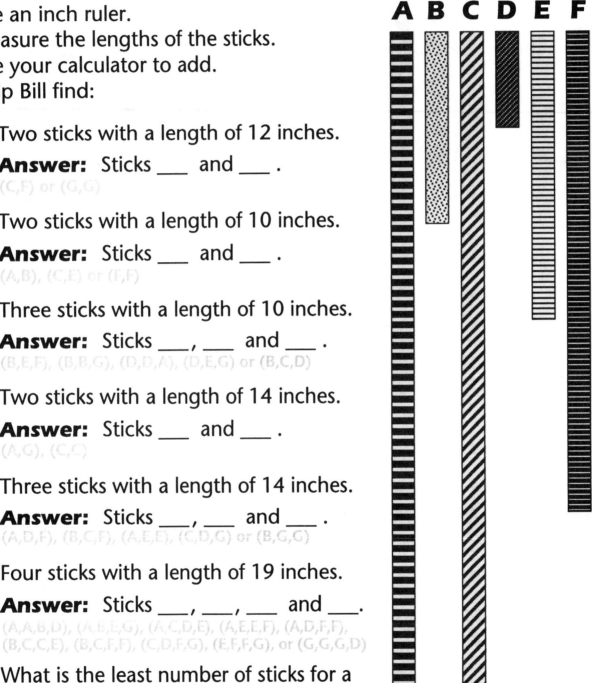

BILL'S STICK FACTORY

A B C D E F G

Use an inch ruler.
Measure the lengths of the sticks.
Use your calculator to add.
Help Bill find:

1. Two sticks with a length of 12 inches.

Answer: Sticks ___ and ___ .

(C,F) or (G,G)

2. Two sticks with a length of 10 inches.

Answer: Sticks ___ and ___ .

(A,B), (C,E) or (F,F)

3. Three sticks with a length of 10 inches.

Answer: Sticks ___ , ___ and ___ .

(B,E,F), (B,B,G), (D,D,A), (D,E,G) or (B,C,D)

4. Two sticks with a length of 14 inches.

Answer: Sticks ___ and ___ .

(A,G), (C,C)

5. Three sticks with a length of 14 inches.

Answer: Sticks ___ , ___ and ___ .

(A,D,F), (B,C,F), (A,E,E), (C,D,G) or (B,G,G)

6. Four sticks with a length of 19 inches.

Answer: Sticks ___ , ___ , ___ and ___ .

(A,A,B,D), (A,B,E,G), (A,C,D,E), (A,E,E,F), (A,D,F,F),
(B,C,C,E), (B,C,F,F), (C,D,F,G), (E,F,F,G), or (G,G,G,D)

7. What is the least number of sticks for a length of 9? Which sticks?

Answer: 2 sticks, (A,D), (B,C) or (E,G)

DITTO THE DIGITS

Maria's paper got wet.

All the numbers are missing from the sequence boxes.

Help her fix her paper. Here is the catch.

For each problem, the same digit goes in each of the empty boxes.

1.

$4 + 4 = \square$ 8.

2.

$2 + 2 + 2 + 2 = \square$ 8.

3.

$1 \; 1 + 1 + 1 = \square$ 13.

4.

$2 \; 2 - 2 - 2 = \square$ 18.

5.

$9 + 9 + 9 = \square$ 27.

6.

$5 + 5 - 5 = \square$ 5.

7.

$2 \; 2 + 2 \; 2 + 2 = \square$ 46.

8.

$4 \; 4 - 4 - 4 = \square$ 36.

9.

$5 \; 5 + 5 + 5 = \square$ 65.

10.

$9 + 9 + 9 + 9 = \square$ 36.

See Lesson Helper, page 73

Ditto the Digits • 17

HIT THE TARGET

Use your calculator.
Can you reach the target number?

		Target	Hit Target?

1. Press: 0 3 Press: **15.** Yes

2. Press: 0 3 **11.** No

3. Press: 1 2 **13.** Yes

4. Press: 1 3 **22.** Yes

5. Press: 0 4 **21.** No

6. Press: 3 5 **33.** Yes

7. Press: 1 6 **37.** Yes

8. Press: 0 8 **56.** Yes

9. Press: 0 + 13 **65.** Yes

10. Press: 1 13 **44.** No

See Lesson Helper, page 73

SHAPE SHOPPING

⬭ 6¢   ◻ 8¢   ▭ 14¢   ⬮ 15¢

How Much For: **Record Display**

1. ⬭ ◻   `0.14`

2. ⬭ ⬭ ◻   `0.20`

3. ⬭ ⬭ ◻ ◻   `0.28`

4. ▭ ▭ ⬭   `0.34`

5. ⬮ ⬮ ◻ ◻   `0.46`

6. ⬮ ⬮ ⬮ ◻ ◻   `0.61`

7. ▭ ⬭ ▭ ⬭ ⬭   `0.46`

8. ⬭ ⬭ ⬭ ▭ ▭   `0.46`

See Lesson Helper, page 74

Shape Shopping • 19

THANKS FOR THE MEMORIES

Key in each sequence.

Copy display.

1.  `3` `M+` `ON/C` `MRC`   *3.*

2. `3` `M+` `M+` `MRC`   *6.*

3.  `3` `M+` `M+` `M+` `MRC`   *9.*

4.  `4` `M+` `5` `M+` `MRC`   *9.*

5.  `8` `M+` `M+` `M+` `MRC`   *24.*

6.  `7` `M+` `3` `M−` `MRC`   *4.*

7. `9` `M+` `4` `M−` `MRC`   *5.*

8. `6` `M+` `M+` `M−` `MRC`   *6.*

ADDITION TRAIN

Use your calculator to put the numbers in the box cars.

261   518   307   223   812   774   119
603   713   496   671   991   183   510

1.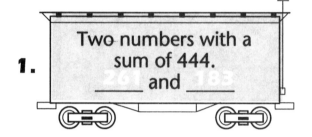
Two numbers with a sum of 444.
_261_ and _183_

2.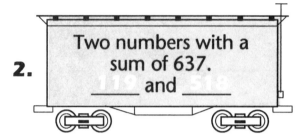
Two numbers with a sum of 637.
_119_ and _518_

3.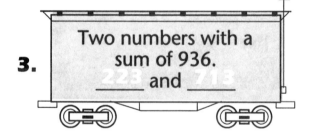
Two numbers with a sum of 936.
_223_ and _713_

4.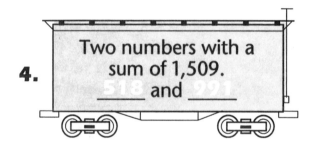
Two numbers with a sum of 1,509.
_518_ and _991_

5.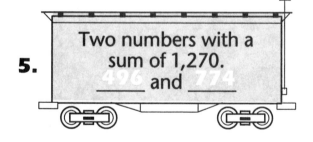
Two numbers with a sum of 1,270.
_496_ and _774_

6.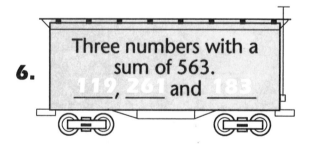
Three numbers with a sum of 563.
_119_, _261_ and _183_

7.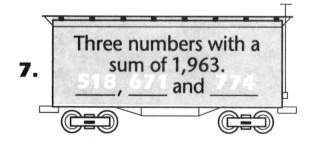
Three numbers with a sum of 1,963.
_518_, _671_ and _774_

8.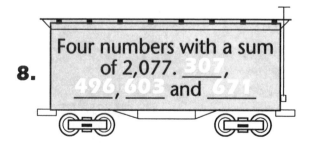
Four numbers with a sum of 2,077. _307_, _496_, _603_ and _671_

See Lesson Helper, page 75

Addition Train • 21

SUM PATHS

RULES
- Add the numbers on your path
- You cannot cross your path
- You must travel up, down, or to the side.
- You cannot travel on the diagonal.

Follow the rules. Make a path to each target number.

1. START

2	5	9	4
6	8	17	2
7	10	3	5
1	6	11	7

TARGET 47

2. START

3	8	6	2
5	18	11	4
7	9	21	15
13	23	14	9

TARGET 81

3. START

24	17	13	15
41	39	27	54
19	27	53	31
26	43	16	21

TARGET 272

4. START

63	27	56	91
84	39	22	41
75	51	43	19
31	87	73	15

TARGET 556

THE MATH MACHINE

What is the math machine doing?

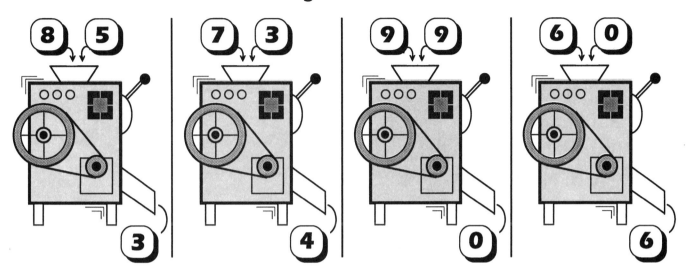

Make your calculator do the same thing. Fill in the blanks.

1. 21 and 16 go in the machine, ___5___ comes out.

2. 33 and 16 go in the machine, ___17___ comes out.

3. 98 and 64 go in the machine, ___34___ comes out.

4. 175 and 103 go in the machine, ___72___ comes out.

5. 543 and 337 go in the machine, ___206___ comes out.

6. 354 and ___0___ go in the machine, 354 comes out.

7. ___712___ and 415 go in the machine, 297 comes out.

8. 1,383 and 1,292 go in the machine, ___91___ comes out.

9. 7,105 and 7,105 go in the machine, ___0___ comes out.

10. _____ and _____ go in the machine, 37 comes out.
Answers will vary.

DISPLAY THE WORDS

Use your calculator.
Match the "words" to the sentences.

1. I cannot tell a _____ .

2. He rang the _____ .

3. She put _____ on her bike chain.

4. The rabbit jumped in the _____ .

5. Mary climbed the _____ .

6. William's dad called him _____ .

7. Joan broke the _____ on her shoe.

8. Maria tried to _____ her old sled.

A. 856 − 146

number

"word" OIL

B. 8936 − 1222

number

"word" hILL

C. 5656 + 2079

number

"word" SELL

D. 3414 + 4304

number

"word" BILL

E. 233 + 84

number

"word" LIE

F. 9793 − 2459

number

"word" hEEL

G. 9215 − 1477

number

"word" BELL

H. 2163 + 1541

number

"word" hOLE

AN OCEAN RIDDLE

Use your calculator to solve the riddle. Place the letters next to displays in the spaces above the same numbers below.

RIDDLE
What kind of ocean creature is sticky when you touch it?

1. 3 X 8 =  **I**

2. 4 X 7 =  **E**

3. 6 X 6 =  **L**

4. 3 X 5 X 4 =  **H**

5. 1 2 X 4 =  **F**

6. 3 X 2 X 7 =  **Y**

7. 2 X 9 X 3 =  **S**

8. 1 3 X 5 =  **L**

9. 4 X 1 7 =  **J**

J E L L Y F I S H
68 28 65 36 42 48 24 54 60

AND THE NUMBER LEFT IS...

Use your calculator to help you solve the problems.
Use each number once.

Use these numbers. ———→

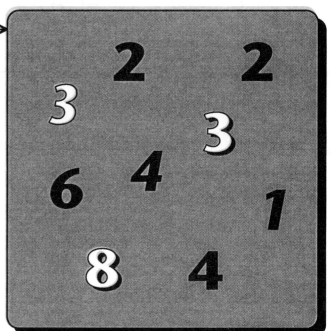

1. Circle two numbers with a product of 12.   ② ⑥

2. Circle two numbers with a product of 8.   ② ④

3. Circle two numbers with a product of 9.   ③ ③

4. Circle two numbers with a product of 4.   ① ④

5. Put an "X" on the number that is left.   ✗

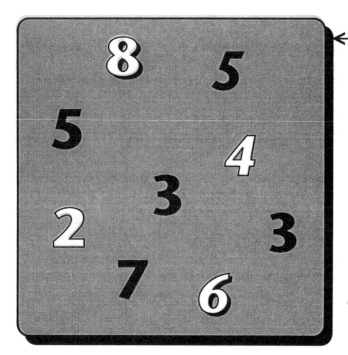

←——— **Use these numbers.**

6. Circle two numbers with a product of 15.   ③ ⑤

7. Circle two numbers with a product of 48.   ⑥ ⑧

8. Circle two numbers with a product of 14.   ② ⑦

9. Circle two numbers with a product of 20.   ④ ⑤

10. Put an "X" on the number that is left.

See Lesson Helper, page 77

PRODUCT PATHS

Follow the rules. Make a path to each target number.

RULES
- Multiply the numbers on your path.
- You cannot cross your path.
- You must travel up, down, or to the side.
- You cannot travel on the diagonal.

1. START

2	1	5	4
4	7	3	0
6	5	1	5
1	2	3	7

TARGET
2,016

2. START

3	1	6	0
5	2	7	4
0	3	4	15
1	2	6	4

TARGET
8,640

3. START

1	4	10	5
2	0	5	2
3	6	3	3
0	7	5	2

TARGET
6,480

4. START

2	1	3	9
2	6	13	2
5	4	0	5
3	9	12	3

TARGET
2,340

See Lesson Helper, page 77

NAME

TARGET TOSS

Can you score on the bean bag boards?

1. Throw three bean bags for a product of 90. __3__ , __5__ , __6__

2. Throw four bean bags for a product of 90. __2__ , __3__ , __3__ , __5__

3. Throw four bean bags for a product of 450. __3__ , __5__ , __5__ , __6__

4. Throw five bean bags for a product of 1,080. __2__ , __3__ , __5__ , __6__ , __6__

5. Throw five bean bags for a product of 1,350. __3__ , __3__ , __5__ , __5__ , __6__

6. Throw three bean bags for a product of 96. __3__ , __4__ , __8__

7. Throw four bean bags for a product of 192. __2__ , __3__ , __4__ , __8__

8. Throw four bean bags for a product of 768. __3__ , __4__ , __8__ , __8__

9. Throw five bean bags for a product of 864. __3__ , __3__ , __3__ , __4__ , __8__

10. Throw five bean bags for a product of 6,144. __3__ , __4__ , __8__ , __8__ , __8__

See Lesson Helper, page 78

A WEATHER RIDDLE

Can you solve the riddle?
Find the missing number for each sequence.
Put the letter that matches each answer in
the correct space below.

RIDDLE
**What kind of
animal can forecast
the weather?**

1. $\boxed{4} \times \boxed{1} \boxed{5} =$ $60.$

2. $\boxed{2} \boxed{4} \div \boxed{3} =$ $8.$

3. $\boxed{1} \boxed{0} \times \boxed{9} =$ $90.$

4. $\boxed{4} \boxed{8} \div \boxed{6} =$ $8.$

5. $\boxed{3} \boxed{5} \div \boxed{7} =$ $5.$

6. $\boxed{1} \boxed{2} \times \boxed{8} =$ $96.$

7. $\boxed{2} \boxed{5} \times \boxed{5} =$ $125.$

8. $\boxed{5} \boxed{4} \div \boxed{9} =$ $6.$

7	3	5	6	12	4	10	9
D	E	E	N	E	R	I	R

R   E   I   N   D   E   E   R
  1.   2.   3.   4.   5.   6.   7.   8.

SOLVE THE MYSTERIES

Use your calculator to help you find the mystery numbers.

1. If you add me to 57, the sum is 103. Who am I?

Answer: 46

2. The product of 29 and me is 899. Who am I?

Answer: 31

3. If you divide me by 11, you get 891. Who am I?

Answer: 9,801

4. Double me and subtract 9 and you get 29. Who am I?

Answer: 19

5. Multiply me by 17 and then add 6. You will get 193. Who am I?

Answer: 11

6. Add me to 7. Then multiply the sum by 8. You will get 128. Who am I?

Answer: 9

7. If you divide 561 by me, the answer is 33. Who am I?

Answer: 17

8. Multiply me by 9. Then add 48. The sum is 507. Who am I?

Answer: 51

9. Add me to 87. Then multiply us by 7. The product is 742. Who am I?

Answer: 19

See Lesson Helper, page 78

FIND THE MATCHES

Find five matches and you are finished.

A. 2 x 4 + 2 x 9	**B.** 65 – 1	**C.** 2 x 7 x 20
D. 3 x 14	**E.** 79 + 87	**F.** 9 x 10 ÷ 18
G. 8 x 7 + 9 x 7	**H.** 14 x 5 x 4	**I.** 16 ÷ 4 + 9
J. 7 x 4 x 5	**K.** (87 + 13) ÷ 25	**L.** 2 x 13
M. 87 + 79	**N.** (5 + 4) x 3	**O.** 8 x 3 x 4
P. 5 x 9 ÷ (7 + 2)	**Q.** 4 x 8 x 3	**R.** 5 x 7 x 4
S. 9 + 4	**T.** 17 x 7	**U.** 8 x 8
V. 14 + 14 + 14	**W.** 3 x 9	**X.** 6 – 2

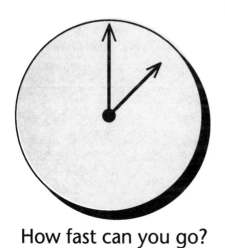

How fast can you go?

Possible matches are:
A and L = 26
B and U = 64
C and H = 280
D and V = 42
E and M = 166
F and P = S
G and T = 119
I and S = 13
J and R = 140
K and X = 4
N and W = 27
O and Q = 96

My matches are:

_____ **and** _____

_____ **and** _____

_____ **and** _____

_____ **and** _____

_____ **and** _____

SCHOOL STORE SALE

BIG SAVINGS-BUY NOW!

Pencils	9¢ each	Notepads	25¢ each	Notebook	60¢ each
Pens	39¢ each	Binders	45¢ each	Felt tip pen	55¢ each
Erasers	6¢ each	Paper	35¢ pack	Tablet	29¢ each

How much for: **Answers**

1. 1 pen and 1 eraser?   **1.** _45¢ or $.45_

2. 2 pens and 2 erasers?   **2.** _90¢ or $.90_

3. 2 erasers and 6 pencils?   **3.** _66¢ or $.66_

4. 2 pens and 3 pencils?   **4.** _105¢ or $1.05_

5. 3 felt tip pens, 2 binders and 1 notepad?   **5.** _280¢ or $2.80_

6. 3 notebooks and 3 pens?   **6.** _297¢ or $2.97_

7. 4 packs of paper, 2 pens and 3 tablets?   **7.** _305¢ or $3.05_

8. Make up your own order.   *Answers will vary*

See Lesson Helper, page 79

REMEMBER ME

Key in each sequence.   **Copy display.**

1. | 2 | X | 1 | 4 | = | M+ |
| 3 | X | 1 | 2 | = | M+ | MRC |

`64.`

2. | 4 | X | 2 | 3 | = | M+ |
| 5 | X | 7 | = | M+ | MRC |

`127.`

3. | 6 | M+ | 1 | 9 | M+ | 8 |
| M− | 1 | 7 | M+ | MRC |

`34.`

4. | 3 | 7 | M+ | 5 | X | 7 | = |
| M+ | 7 | M+ | MRC |

`79.`

---

5. Mary bought 3 apples at 27 cents each and 2 oranges at 33 cents each. How much did she spend altogether?

147¢ or $1.47

6. Luis bought 7 pencils at 19 cents each and 3 erasers at 8 cents each. How much did he spend altogether?

157¢ or $1.57

7. Victor's mother gave him $5 for 3 tickets for the school play. If tickets cost $1.45 each, how much change did he give his mother?

65¢ or $.65

8. *Shopping List*
2 cans juice at 75¢ each
1 box of cereal at 95¢ each
3 loaves of bread at $1.25 each

How much change from a $10 bill?

380¢ or $3.80

See Lesson Helper, page 80

Remember Me • 33

FRUIT SHOPPING

Use your calculator to total each order.

FRED'S FRUIT STAND
"Fresh Fruit is our Business"

Apples	89¢ lb.	Bananas	49¢ lb.	Super Buy On
Oranges	4/$1.30	Pears	89¢ lb.	Strawberries
Grapefruit	2/$1.00	Watermelon	29¢ lb.	Blueberries
Grapes	99¢ lb.	Lemons	4/$1.50	by the pint
				Each $1.30 a pint

Cantaloupes...99¢ each   Pineapples...$1.80 each

ORDER 1
3 lb. Apples — $2.67
4 Oranges — $1.30
2 lb. Bananas — $0.98
I pint Strawberries — $1.30

Total Cost — $6.25

ORDER 2
3 Pineapples — $5.40
12 Lemons — $4.50
2 lb. Grapes — $1.98
3 lb. Pears — $2.67

Total Cost — $14.55

ORDER 3
10 lb. Watermelon — $2.90
3 Grapefruits — $1.50
5 lb. Apples — $4.45

Total Cost — $8.85

ORDER 4
4 Cantaloupes — $3.96
3 pints Blueberries — $3.90
2 lb. Bananas — $0.98
1 Grapefruit — $0.50

Total Cost — $9.34

ORDER 5
8 Lemons — $3.00
2 Pineapples — $3.60
7 lb. Apples — $6.23

Total Cost — $12.83

ORDER 6
3 Cantaloupes — $2.97
4 lb. Bananas — $1.96
8 Oranges — $2.60

Total Cost — $7.53

ORDER 7
9 lb. Watermelon — $2.61
2 pints Strawberries — $2.60
3 lb. Grapes — $2.97

Total Cost — $8.18

ORDER 8
6 lb. Apples — $5.34
12 Oranges — $3.90
3 lb. Pears — $2.67
3 lb. Grapes — $2.97
8 Lemons — $3.00

Total Cost — $17.88

ORDER 9
2 pints Blueberries — $2.60
3 pints Strawberries — $3.90
4 lb. Apples — $3.56
6 lb. Bananas — $2.94
2 Pineapples — $3.60
4 lb. Pears — $3.56

Total Cost — $20.16

See Lesson Helper, page 80

PLACE VALUE CHECK

Use your calculator and the numbers below.
Follow the directions to answer the question.

1,649   5,942   21,391   51,211   837   617   908
267,914   27,564   300,103   217,658   273

1. Find the sum of all the five-digit numbers.   **1.** __100,166__

2. Find the sum of all the numbers with a 2 in them.   **2.** __591,953__

3. Find the sum of all the numbers with a 4 in the tens' place.   **3.** __7,591__

4. Find the sum of all the numbers with a 6 in the hundred's place.   **4.** __219,924__

5. Find the sum of all the numbers with a 2 in the hundred thousands' place.   **5.** __485,572__

6. Subtract the smallest number from the largest number.   **6.** __299,830__

7. Find the sum of all your answers.   **7.** __1,705,036__

8. Add 3,674,873 to the last answer.   **8.** __5,379,909__

> **Turn your calculator upside down.**
> **Read the word in your display for the**
> **answer to the question.**

> **What do scuba**
> **divers wear?**

NAME

MORE SUM PATHS

Follow the rules. Make a path to each target number.

RULES
- Add the numbers on your path.
- You cannot cross your path
- You must travel up, down, or to the side.
- You cannot travel on the diagonal.

1. START

12	17	27	15
23	9	0	7
31	11	13	25
41	8	24	19

TARGET 122

2. START

28	12	34	25
53	11	37	81
36	55	61	23
21	81	33	18

TARGET 231

3. START

104	254	90	71
210	56	209	44
631	82	111	227
263	752	72	106

TARGET 741

4. START

21	105	99	87
66	901	527	324
39	784	293	81
51	325	502	63

TARGET 2806

See Lesson Helper, page 81

More Sum Paths • **36**

PRODUCT SEARCH

Choose from the ten digits.
Follow the directions to form the
largest or smallest possible products.

Choose from:

0, 1, 2, 3, 4, 5, 6, 7, 8, 9

1. Largest possible product:
__ __ __ × __

2. Largest possible product:
__ __ × __ __

3. Largest possible product:
__ __ __ × __ __

4. Largest possible product:
__ __ __ × __ __ __

5. Largest possible product:
__ __ __ __ × __ __

6. Smallest possible product:
__ __ × __ __

7. Smallest possible product:
__ __ × __ __ __

8. Largest possible odd product:
__ __ × __ __ __

9. Smallest possible even product:
__ __ __ × __ __ __

10. Smallest possible odd product:
__ × __ __ __

1. _____

2. _____

3. _____

4. _____

5. _____

6. _____

7. _____

8. _____

9. _____

10. _____

SEARCHING FOR PATTERNS

Find the next three numbers
in each of the patterns.

1. 1, 2, 4, 8, 16, ____ , ____ , ____ , ...

2. 3, 9, 27, 81, 243, ____ , ____ , ____ , ...

3. 7, 16, 34, 70, 142, ____ , ____ , ____ , ...

4. 1, 4, 13, 40, 121, ____ , ____ , ____ , ...

5. 2, 5, 10, 17, 26, ____ , ____ , ____ , ...

6. 0, 7, 26, 63, 124, ____ , ____ , ____ , ...

7. 1, 6, 26, 86, 106, ____ , ____ , ____ , ...

8. 1, 4, 10, 22, 46, ____ , ____ , ____ , ...

9. 1, 10, 37, 118, 361, ____ , ____ , ____ , ...

10. 1, 10, 55, 280, 1,405, ____ , ____ , ____ , ...

11. 1, 9, 33, 105, 321, ____ , ____ , ____ , ...

12. 1, 7, 61, 547, 4,921, ____ , ____ , ____ , ...

13. 1, 4, 9, 61, 52, ____ , ____ , ____ , ...

14. 3, 3, 5, 4, 4, ____ , ____ , ____ , ...

15. 8, 5, 4, 9, 1, ____ , ____ , ____ , ...

NAME

ANOTHER MATH MACHINE

What is the machine doing?

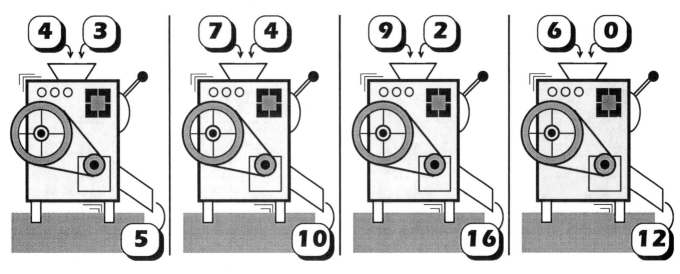

Make your calculator do the same thing. Fill in the blanks.

1. 13 and 8 go in the machine, _____ comes out.

2. 16 and 11 go in the machine, _____ comes out.

3. 33 and 21 go in the machine, _____ comes out.

4. 154 and 93 go in the machine, _____ comes out.

5. 165 and 49 go in the machine, _____ comes out.

6. 45 and _____ go in the machine, 53 comes out.

7. _____ and 71 go in the machine, 357 comes out.

8. 365 and 730 go in the machine, _____ comes out.

9. 224 and 0 go in the machine, _____ comes out.

10. _____ and _____ go in the machine, 18 comes out.

MORE PRODUCT PATHS

Follow the rules. Make a path
to each target number.

RULES

- Multiply the numbers on your path.
- You cannot cross your path.
- You must travel up, down, or to the side.
- You cannot travel on the diagonal.

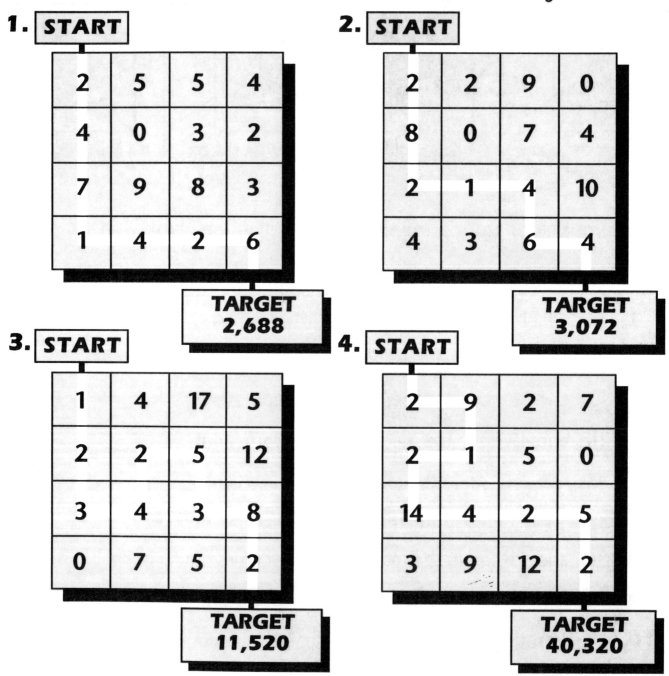

1. START

2	5	5	4
4	0	3	2
7	9	8	3
1	4	2	6

TARGET
2,688

2. START

2	2	9	0
8	0	7	4
2	1	4	10
4	3	6	4

TARGET
3,072

3. START

1	4	17	5
2	2	5	12
3	4	3	8
0	7	5	2

TARGET
11,520

4. START

2	9	2	7
2	1	5	0
14	4	2	5
3	9	12	2

TARGET
40,320

See Lesson paper page 63

NAME

DIVISION SPRINT

Complete the division problems.
Use the numbers at the right.
Use each number once.
How fast can you go?

Use these numbers.

15 16 28 34 52 64 85
94 272 345 512 572
784 812 1,728 1,785
1,905 2,352 3,105 3,196

1. 1728 ÷ 64 = 27

2. 1905 ÷ 15 = 127

3. 3196 ÷ 94 = 34

4. 1785 ÷ 85 = 21

5. 272 ÷ 34 = 8

6. 2352 ÷ 784 = 3

7. 572 ÷ 52 = 11

8. 3105 ÷ 345 = 9

9. 812 ÷ 28 = 29

10. 512 ÷ 16 = 32

Start time _____

Finish time _____

See Lesson Helper, page 83

Division Sprint • 41

© STOKES PUBLISHING COMPANY

WACKY WORDS

Complete the computations to obtain the "words."

C O M P U T A T I O N

1. 2,587 + _2_,_9__2__1_
2. _8__1_,_1__6_8_ – 3,823
3. _1__2_,_6__9__3_ × 3
4. 14 × ___1_1_
5. 221 × _3__5_
6. _____ + vary _____
7. __ __,__ __4_ ÷ 8
8. 1,272 – _____
9. __,_____ – _____
10. ___ Answers will vary ÷ __ __
11. 15,929 ÷ ___
12. ___,_____ – _____

Word in Display

1. `8055`
2. `5hELL`
3. `6LOBE`
4. `hI LL`
5. `5ELL`
6. `8I 6`
7. `8ELL`
8. `LO6`
9. `hI 55`
10. `hOE`
11. `LE6`
12. `hOLE`

$$\begin{array}{r} 198 \\ +119 \\ \hline 317 \end{array}$$ LIE

See Lesson Helper, page 83

Wacky Words • **42**

NAME _____

FAST MATH

Find the answers as fast as you can.

1. 27 x 6 _____

2. 36 + 64 _____

3. 61 – 31 _____

4. 16 x 2 _____

5. 16 x 20 _____

6. 16 x 200 _____

7. 176 + 279 + 387 _____

8. 88 ÷ 4 _____

9. 5 x 37 x 2 _____

10. 200 ÷ 5 _____

11. 11,704 – 7,897 _____

12. 4 x 3 + 4 x 7 _____

13. 8,167 + 5,897 + 439 _____

14. 140 ÷ 70 _____

15. 172 – 71 _____

16. 523 x 73 _____

17. 6,612 ÷ 87 _____

18. 30 x 30 _____

19. 142 + 58 _____

20. 97 x 67 + 3 x 67 _____

21. 278 + 122 _____

22. 677 – 277 _____

23. 200 + 20 + 2 _____

24. 2 x 99 _____

25. 4 x 17 x 5 _____

26. 5,811 ÷ 39 _____

27. 9 x 39 + 39 _____

28. 28 + 397 + 72 _____

29. 3,000 ÷ 3 _____

30. 3,000 ÷ 30 _____

A PET RIDDLE

Use your calculator to simplify each expression. Solve the riddle by placing each letter next to the answers in the spaces below.

RIDDLE:
What geographic location is like a household pet?

1. $18 \times 6 + 17 =$
2. $15 \times 9 + 16 =$
3. $91 \div 7 + 1 =$
4. $21 \times 13 + 6 \times 23 =$
5. $(19 \times 4 + 12) \times 5 =$
6. $24 \times 13 - 7 \times 38 =$
7. $(39 + 17 \times 11) \times 3 =$
8. $4 \times 142 + 45 \times 8 =$
9. $392 \div 7 - 315 \div 7 =$
10. $(97 + 21) \times (64 - 57) =$
11. $1{,}350 \div 225 \times 21 =$
12. $17 \times 19 + 168 \div 42 =$

1. ____ N
2. ____ L
3. ____ N
4. ____ R
5. ____ S
6. ____ Y
7. ____ D
8. ____ I
9. ____ A
10. ____ C
11. ____ A
12. ____ A

THE __ __ __ __ __ __   __ __ __ __ __ __ S
826 126 125 327 411 46   928 440 151 11 14 678

See Lesson Plan

SHORT STROKES

Use your calculator to reach the target numbers. The catch?
Do it with the **least** number of keystrokes. Answers may vary.

Digits to Use	Sequence	Target Number
1. 3		9.
2. 4		12.
3. 7		56.
4. 3, 4		36.
5. 0, 2		218.
6. 1, 7		68.
7. 1, 2, 3		44.
8. 5, 9		256.
9. 3, 7		158.
10. 2, 9		731.

NAME

EXPONENTS AND PROBLEM SOLVING

Find the missing numbers.

1. $\boxed{4}^5 = 1{,}024$

2. $\boxed{7}^3 = 343$

3. $\boxed{8}^4 = 4{,}096$

4. $\boxed{6}^4 = 1{,}296$

5. $\boxed{11}^3 = 1{,}331$

6. $\boxed{}^5 = 59{,}049$

7. $\boxed{3}^6 = 729$

8. $\boxed{}^4 = 38{,}416$

9. $\boxed{2}^7 = 128$

10. $\boxed{4}^8 = 65{,}536$

11. $\boxed{47}^2 = 2{,}209$

12. $\boxed{17}^3 = 4{,}913$

13. $\boxed{61}^2 = 3{,}721$

14. $\boxed{18}^4 = 104{,}976$

15. $\boxed{7}^5 = 16{,}807$

16. $\boxed{27}^3 = 19{,}683$

17. $\boxed{19}^4 = 130{,}321$

18. $\boxed{31}^3 = 29{,}791$

19. $\boxed{13}^6 = 4{,}826{,}809$

20. $\boxed{14}^5 = 537{,}824$

NUMBER PYRAMIDS

Find the missing numbers in the pyramids.

1.

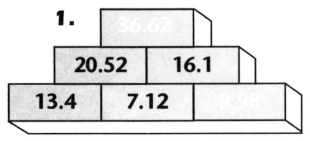

36.62

20.52 | 16.1

13.4 | 7.12 | 6.98

Guess the operation.

2.

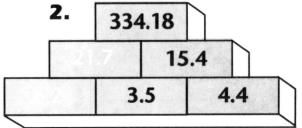

334.18

21.7 | 15.4

3.5 | 4.4

Guess the operation.

3.

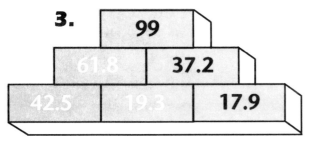

99

61.8 | 37.2

42.5 | 19.3 | 17.9

Use addition.

4.

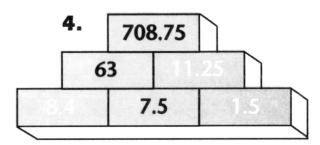

708.75

63 | 11.25

8.4 | 7.5 | 1.5

Use multiplication.

5.

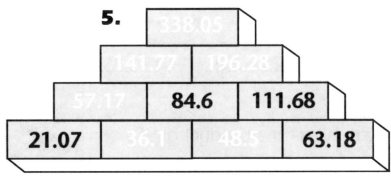

338.05

141.77 | 196.28

57.17 | 84.6 | 111.68

21.07 | 36.1 | 48.5 | 63.18

Use addition.

ANOTHER TARGET TOSS

Can you score on the bean bag boards?

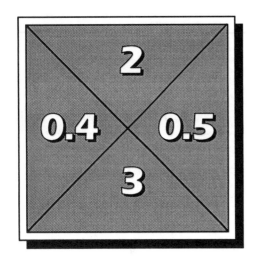

1. Throw three bean bags for a product of 2.

___ , ___ , ___

2. Throw three bean bags for a product of 0.4.

___ , ___ , ___

3. Throw four bean bags for a product of 1.2.

___ , ___ , ___ , ___

4. Throw five bean bags for a product of 3.6.

___ , ___ , ___ , ___ , ___

5. Throw five bean bags for a product of 0.6.

___ , ___ , ___ , ___ , ___

6. Throw three bean bags for a product of 20.4.

___ , ___ , ___

7. Throw four bean bags for a product of 51.

___ , ___ , ___ , ___

8. Throw four bean bags for a product of 156.25.

___ , ___ , ___ , ___

9. Throw five bean bags for a product of 90.

___ , ___ , ___ , ___ , ___

10. Throw five bean bags for a product of 86.7.

___ , ___ , ___ , ___ , ___

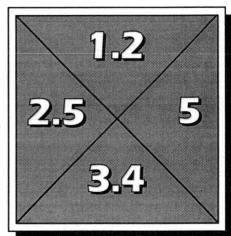

FIND THE OPERATIONS

Find the missing operations.

1. 3 × 7 + 6 = | 27.
2. 3 × 7 ÷ 6 = | 3.5
3. . 8 × 3 2 = | 25.6
4. 3 . 4 × 1 5 = | 51.
5. 2 . 8 × 9 = | 25.2
6. . 4 + 5 − 3 = | 2.4
7. 6 ÷ . 3 × 9 = | 180.
8. 1 2 ÷ 8 + 8 = | 9.5
9. 5 × 7 . 2 = | 36.
10. 2 . 5 ÷ = = = | 0.064
11. 4 ÷ 5 × 8 = | 6.4
12. 1 5 × 3 ÷ 8 = | 5.625

Find the Operations • 49

NAME _____

DECIMAL PATTERNS

Find the next three numbers in each
of the patterns.

1. 1, 1.07, 1.14, 1.21, 1.28, 1.35 , 1.42 , 1.49 , ...

2. 0, 3.5, 7, 10.5, 14, 17.5 , 21 , 24.5 , ...

3. 1, 2.25, 4.75, 9.75, 19.75, 39.75 , 79.75 , 159.75 , ...

4. 30, 15, 7.5, 3.75, 1.875, 0.9375 , 0.46875 , 0.234375 , ...

5. 200, 300, 450, 675, 1,012.5, 1518.75 , 2278.125 , 3417.1875 , ...

6. 0.3125, 0.625, 1.25, 2.5, 5, 10 , 20 , 40 , ...

7. 1, 1.5, 2.5, 4.5, 8.5, 16.5 , 32.5 , 64.5 , ...

8. 1, 3.5, 8.5, 18.5, 38.5, 78.5 , 158.5 , 318.5 , ...

9. 1, 6.5, 12, 17.5, 23, 28.5 , 34 , 39.5 , ...

10. 1, 2.5, 7, 20.5, 61, 182.5 , 547 , 1640.5 , ...

11. 0.5, 3.5, 9.5, 21.5, 45.5, 93.5 , 189.5 , 381.5 , ...

12. 0.5, 2, 5, 11, 23, 47 , 95 , 191 , ...

13. 1, 4.75, 16, 49.75, 151, 454.75 , 1366 , 4099.75 , ...

14. 1, 3, 7, 15, 31, 63 , 127 , 255 , ...

15. 1, 4.75, 19.75, 79.75, 319.75, 1279.75 , 5119.75 , 20479.75 , ...

© STOKES PUBLISHING COMPANY

SHOPPING FOR FRUIT AND VEGGIES

Use your calculator to total each order.

VIC'S VEGGIE & FRUIT CART
TODAY'S SPECIALS

Lettuce	79¢ lb.	Celery	99¢ ea.	Fresh Squash	99¢ lb.
Lemons	5/$1.69	Peaches	$1.49 lb.	Asparagus	$2.98 lb.
Avocados	2/$3.00	Apples	99¢ lb.	Limes	5/$1.25
Apricots	$1.98 lb.	Green Beans	59¢ lb.	Pears	$1.45 lb.

Red Potatoes...2 lb. for $1 ▪ **Navel Oranges...12 for $1.99**

ORDER 1
4 Avocados ____
2 lb. Apricots ____
4 lb. Apples ____
3 lb. Green Beans ____
Total Cost ____

ORDER 2
12 Oranges ____
5 Limes ____
2 lb. Asparagus ____
2 lb. Pears ____
Total Cost ____

ORDER 3
2 lb. Lettuce ____
10 Lemons ____
3 lb. Squash ____
4 lb. Apples ____
Total Cost ____

ORDER 4
6 Oranges ____
5 Limes ____
3 lb. Squash ____
3 lb. Lettuce ____
Total Cost ____

ORDER 5
4 lb. Peaches ____
3 lb. Apples ____
2 Celery ____
Total Cost ____

ORDER 6
3 lb. Apricots ____
2 lb. Asparagus ____
3 lb. Pears ____
Total Cost ____

ORDER 7
4 lb. Green Beans ____
6 lb. Potatoes ____
3 lb. Pears ____
Total Cost ____

ORDER 8
3 lb. Lettuce ____
5 Lemons ____
3 lb. Peaches ____
2 lb. Apricots ____
5 Limes ____
Total Cost ____

ORDER 9
4 lb. Squash ____
3 lb. Asparagus ____
1 lb. Apricots ____
4 lb. Apples ____
3 Celery ____
Total Cost ____

DECIMAL MAZE

Find the way from **START** to **FINISH**. You must find and follow a pattern to get through the maze. Watch for "blind alleys."

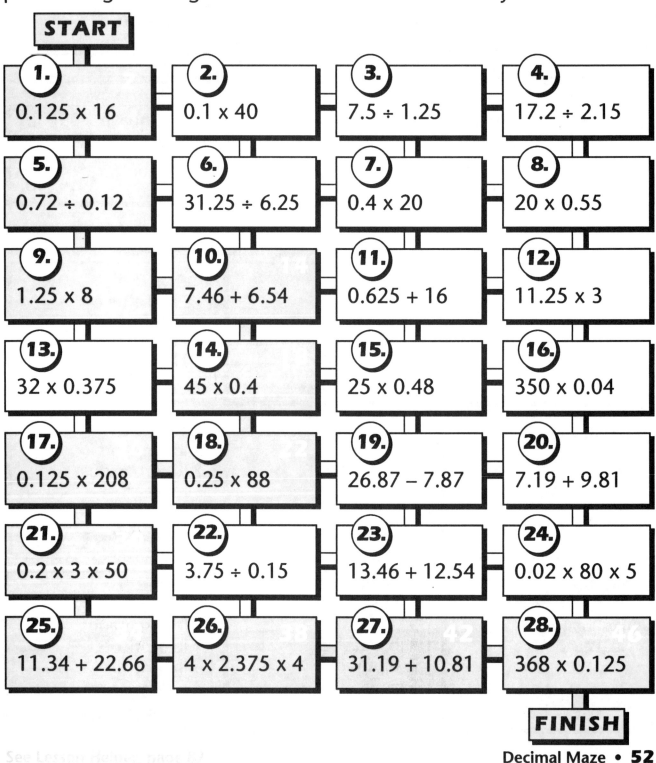

START

1. 0.125 x 16	2. 0.1 x 40	3. 7.5 ÷ 1.25	4. 17.2 ÷ 2.15
5. 0.72 ÷ 0.12	6. 31.25 ÷ 6.25	7. 0.4 x 20	8. 20 x 0.55
9. 1.25 x 8	10. 7.46 + 6.54	11. 0.625 + 16	12. 11.25 x 3
13. 32 x 0.375	14. 45 x 0.4	15. 25 x 0.48	16. 350 x 0.04
17. 0.125 x 208	18. 0.25 x 88	19. 26.87 – 7.87	20. 7.19 + 9.81
21. 0.2 x 3 x 50	22. 3.75 ÷ 0.15	23. 13.46 + 12.54	24. 0.02 x 80 x 5
25. 11.34 + 22.66	26. 4 x 2.375 x 4	27. 31.19 + 10.81	28. 368 x 0.125

FINISH

DECIMAL DETECTIVE

Use your calculator to help you find the
mystery numbers.

1. If you add me
to 14.7, the sum is
52.6. Who am I?

Answer: 37.9

2. The product of
3.75 and me is
67.5. Who am I?

Answer: 18

3. If you divide me
by 1.8, you get
140.4. Who am I?

Answer: 252.72

4. Triple me and
add 5 and
you get 30.5.
Who am I?

Answer: 8.5

5. Multiply me by
4.5 and then add
37. You will get
42.4. Who am I?

Answer: 1.2

6. Add me to 3.75.
Then multiply the
sum by 8. You will
get 36. Who am I?

Answer: 0.75

7. If you divide
27.5 by me, the
answer is 55.
Who am I?

Answer: 0.5

8. Multiply me by
3.25. Then add 9.
The sum is 22.325.
Who am I?

Answer: 4.1

9. Add me to 82.56.
Then multiply us
by 0.5. The product
is 100. Who am I?

Answer: 117.44

FIND THE MATCHES

Find five matches and you are finished.

A. 17 × 29 – 3

B. (90 – 6.7) × 0.75

C. 36 × 12.5 ÷ 90

D. 150% of 85

E. 7 × 13 + 19 × 13

F. 184.5 – 7 × 13

G. 36 ÷ 50 × 80

H. 152 × 0.25 × 47

I. 8 ÷ (2 ÷ 8)

J. 450 ÷ 90

K. 75% of 160

L. 17.9 × 6

M. (100 – 82.1) × 6

N. $\frac{3}{8}$ × 48

O. 83.3 × $\frac{3}{4}$

P. 48 × 0.375

Q. 35 × 6 + 35 × 8

R. 0.72 × 80

S. 47 × 38

T. 3 × 61.5 – 7 × 13

U. 85 × 1.5

V. 160 × (1 – 0.25)

W. 26 × 13

X. 8 × 4

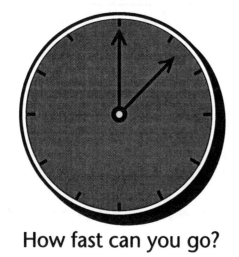

How fast can you go?

Possible matches
are:
A and Q
B and O
C and J
D and U
E and W
F and T
G and R
H and S
I and X
K and V
L and M
N and P

My matches are:

___ and ___

___ and ___

___ and ___

___ and ___

___ and ___

MORE SHORT STROKES

Use your calculator to reach the target numbers. The catch?
Do it with the **least** number of keystrokes. Answers may vary.

Digits to Use	Sequence	Target Number
1. 1,8	1 ÷ 8 =	0.125
2. 3,5	5 – 3 ÷ 5 =	0.4
3. 0,2 and ⊡	2 x . 0 2 = =	0.08
4. 6,8	6 + 6 ÷ 8 =	1.5
5. 3,5 and ⊡	3 . 5 x =	12.25
6. 0,7 and ⊡	7 x . 0 7 =	0.49
7. 4,5	5 ÷ 4 = =	0.3125
8. 1,4,7	7 – 1 ÷ 4 =	1.5
9. 3 and ⊡	. 3 x 3 = =	0.27
10. 1,4 and ⊡	1 ÷ . 4 =	2.5

See Lesson Helper, page 89

More Short Strokes • **55**

COLUMN MATH

Complete the equations.
Choose a number from Column I and
a number from Column II.

Column I	Column II	Equations
1. 19.5	**A.** 0.25	**a.** 1.45 x 7 = 10.15
2. 23	**B.** 52	**b.** 2.7 + 2.45 = 5.15
3. 18	**C.** 140	**c.** $\frac{3}{8}$ x 420 = 157.5
4. 17	**D.** 7	**d.** 18 ÷ 1.2 = 15
5. 3.7	**E.** 6.5	**e.** 65 ÷ 6.5 = 10
6. 3/8	**F.** 2.45	**f.** $\frac{2}{5}$ x 140 = 56
7. 28	**G.** 4.5	**g.** 19.5 + 30.25 = 49.75
8. 1.45	**H.** 1.2	**h.** 17 − 15.2 = 1.8
9. 2/5	**I.** 30.25	**i.** 23 x 1.4 = 32.2
10. 2.7	**J.** 420	**j.** 13 ÷ 52 = 0.25
11. 65	**K.** 1.4	**k.** 3.7 x 4.5 = 16.65
12. 13	**L.** 15.2	**l.** 28 ÷ 0.25 = 112

See Lesson Helper, page 89

PERCENT MAZE

Find the way from **START** to **FINISH**. You must find and follow a pattern to get through the maze. Watch for "blind alleys."

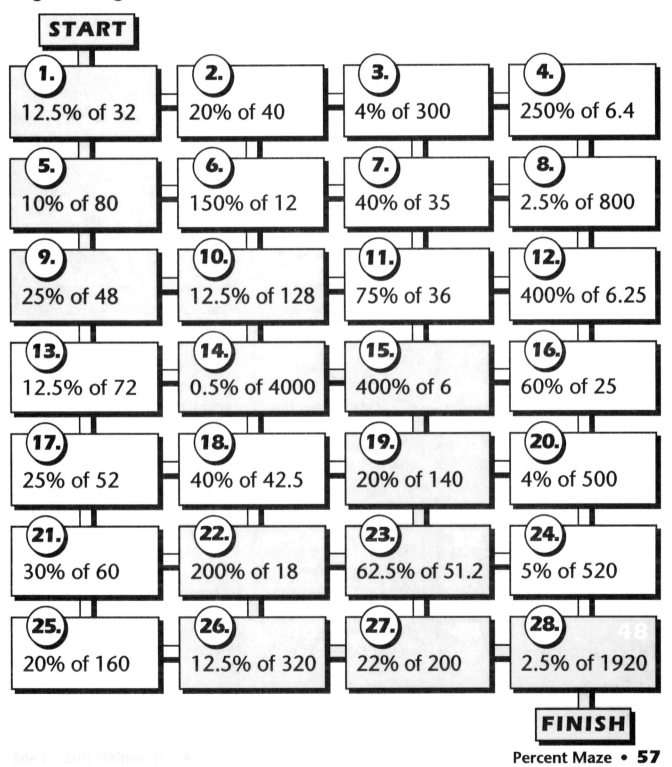

START

1. 12.5% of 32	**2.** 20% of 40	**3.** 4% of 300	**4.** 250% of 6.4
5. 10% of 80	**6.** 150% of 12	**7.** 40% of 35	**8.** 2.5% of 800
9. 25% of 48	**10.** 12.5% of 128	**11.** 75% of 36	**12.** 400% of 6.25
13. 12.5% of 72	**14.** 0.5% of 4000	**15.** 400% of 6	**16.** 60% of 25
17. 25% of 52	**18.** 40% of 42.5	**19.** 20% of 140	**20.** 4% of 500
21. 30% of 60	**22.** 200% of 18	**23.** 62.5% of 51.2	**24.** 5% of 520
25. 20% of 160	**26.** 12.5% of 320	**27.** 22% of 200	**28.** 2.5% of 1920

FINISH

BOB'S BIKE BARN

If it has wheels, Bob has it. Check out this week's specials.

20 in. bike $79.99	24 in. 10 speed $139.99	16 in. youth bike $59.99
red wagon $29.99	tricycle $44.99	skateboard $45.99
rugged mountain bike $179.99	deluxe mountain bike $239.99	fiberglass skateboard $99.99

1. Jill took her mother to Walt's. She bought a fiberglass skateboard for 20% off the ticket price. How much did she pay?

Answer _____

2. Mr. Garcia purchased a 20 in. bike and a 16 in. youth bike. His bill was discounted 15%. How much did he pay?

Answer _____

3. Mrs. Daws bought a rugged mountain bike at 15% off and a tricycle at regular price. How much did she pay?

Answer _____

4. Carlos' father received a 25% discount on the purchase of a 24 in. 10 speed, a red wagon, and a skateboard. How much did he pay?

Answer _____

5. All deluxe mountain bikes will be marked up 12% next week. What will be the new price?

Answer _____

6. A dealer bought three 20 in. bikes and five 16 in. youth bikes and received a 25% discount on the puchase. How much did he pay?

Answer _____

NAME _____

MORE FAST MATH

Find the answers as fast as you can.

1. 27.43 x 63.7 _____   **16.** 31.29 x 10 _____

2. 0.5 x 80 _____   **17.** 13 ÷ 0.5 _____

3. 17 – 15.5 _____   **18.** 300 x 0.1 _____

4. 1.4 x 5 _____   **19.** 300 x 0.01 _____

5. 1.4 x 50 _____   **20.** 2 x 4.3 + 98 x 4.3 _____

6. 1.4 x 500 _____   **21.** 150% of 18 _____

7. 53.8 + 74.9 + 186.17 _____   **22.** $\frac{3}{4}$ x 40 _____

8. 0.75 ÷ 0.75 _____   **23.** 0.75 x 40 _____

9. 2.5 x 57 x 4 _____   **24.** 4.89 x 8.7 _____

10. $\frac{1}{4}$ x 400 _____   **25.** 0.1 x 150 _____

11. 30% of 40 _____   **26.** 163.54 ÷ 1.5 _____

12. 3.7 x 4 + 3.7 x 6 _____   **27.** 10% of 79 _____

13. 59.41 + 3.767 + 134.36 _____   **28.** 153.45 – 53.45 _____

14. $\frac{1}{2} + \frac{7}{8} + \frac{1}{2}$ _____   **29.** 16 ÷ 0.1 _____

15. 27.03 – 1.03 _____   **30.** 16 ÷ 0.01 _____

CHANGE THE SIGNS

Complete each sequence by finding the missing numbers.

Display

1. [8] [+] [3] [+/−] [=]   [_5.]

2. [3] [+] [+/−] [8] [=]   [5.]

3. [3] [+/−] [+] [4] [+/−] [=]   [- 7.]

4. [2] [2] [+/−] [+] [7] [=]   [- 15.]

5. [7] [+/−] [+] [2] [2] [=]   [15.]

6. [6] [+] [4] [+/−] [+] [9] [=]   [11.]

7. [2] [5] [+/−] [+] [1] [9] [=]   [- 6.]

8. [2] [+] [6] [+] [8] [+/−] [=]   [0.]

9. [ ] [+] [ ] [+/−] [=]   [8.]

(9,1), (8,0)

10. [ ] [+] [ ] [+/−] [=]   [- 5.]

(0,5), (1,6), (2,7), (3,8), (4,9)

EXPONENT EXPLORATIONS

Find the missing numbers.

1. $\boxed{7}^{2} + 1 = 50$

2. $\boxed{6}^{2} - 7 = 29$

3. $\boxed{4}^{3} \times 2 = 128$

4. $\boxed{10}^{2} \div 2 = 50$

5. $\boxed{2}^{5} - 1 = 31$

6. $\boxed{3}^{3} \times 2 = 54$

7. $\boxed{7}^{2} - 17 = 32$

8. $\boxed{4}^{4} + 10 = 266$

9. $\boxed{12}^{2} - 14 = 130$

10. $\boxed{6}^{3} \div 216 = 1$

11. $\boxed{1}^{2} \div 4 = 0.25$

12. $\boxed{7}^{3} + 7 = 350$

13. $\boxed{3}^{4} \div 9 = 9$

14. $\boxed{2}^{2} \div 0.25 = 16$

15. $\boxed{.5}^{2} + 0.25 = 0.5$

16. $\boxed{9}^{3} + 1 = 730$

17. $\boxed{2.5}^{2} \times 2 = 12.5$

18. $\boxed{8}^{4} + 4 = 4,100$

19. $\boxed{2}^{6} \times 4 = 256$

20. $\boxed{1}^{4} + 8 = 9$

MATCH THE COLUMNS

Sequence	Expression
1. $\boxed{2}$ $\boxed{5}$ $\boxed{\sqrt{}}$	**a.** $\sqrt{112+9}$
2. $\boxed{4}$ $\boxed{9}$ $\boxed{\sqrt{}}$	**b.** $\sqrt{16}-\sqrt{9}$
3. $\boxed{2}$ $\boxed{0}$ $\boxed{+}$ $\boxed{1}$ $\boxed{6}$ $\boxed{=}$ $\boxed{\sqrt{}}$	**c.** $\sqrt{64}\div 2$
4. $\boxed{2}$ $\boxed{0}$ $\boxed{+}$ $\boxed{1}$ $\boxed{6}$ $\boxed{\sqrt{}}$ $\boxed{=}$	**d.** $\sqrt{25}$
5. $\boxed{8}$ $\boxed{1}$ $\boxed{\sqrt{}}$ $\boxed{+}$ $\boxed{7}$ $\boxed{=}$	**e.** $9+\sqrt{16}$
6. $\boxed{6}$ $\boxed{4}$ $\boxed{\sqrt{}}$ $\boxed{\div}$ $\boxed{2}$ $\boxed{=}$	**f.** $\sqrt{20+16}$
7. $\boxed{3}$ $\boxed{X}$ $\boxed{=}$ $\boxed{-}$ $\boxed{5}$ $\boxed{=}$ $\boxed{\sqrt{}}$	**g.** $112+\sqrt{9}$
8. $\boxed{4}$ $\boxed{X}$ $\boxed{2}$ $\boxed{5}$ $\boxed{\sqrt{}}$ $\boxed{=}$	**h.** $\sqrt{3^2-5}$
9. $\boxed{1}$ $\boxed{1}$ $\boxed{2}$ $\boxed{+}$ $\boxed{9}$ $\boxed{=}$ $\boxed{\sqrt{}}$	**i.** $20+\sqrt{16}$
10. $\boxed{1}$ $\boxed{1}$ $\boxed{2}$ $\boxed{+}$ $\boxed{9}$ $\boxed{\sqrt{}}$ $\boxed{=}$	**j.** $\sqrt{81}+7$
11. $\boxed{1}$ $\boxed{6}$ $\boxed{\sqrt{}}$ $\boxed{-}$ $\boxed{9}$ $\boxed{\sqrt{}}$ $\boxed{=}$	**k.** $4\sqrt{25}$
12. $\boxed{9}$ $\boxed{+}$ $\boxed{1}$ $\boxed{6}$ $\boxed{\sqrt{}}$ $\boxed{=}$	**l.** $\sqrt{49}$

My matches are:

1. __d.__   2. __l.__   3. __f.__   4. __i.__   5. __j.__   6. __c.__

7. __h.__   8. __k.__   9. __a.__   10. __g.__   11. __b.__   12. __e.__

RIGHT TRIANGLE STUFF

Find the lengths of the missing sides.

1.

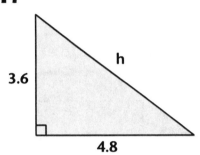

h = ___6___

2.

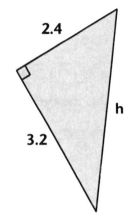

h = ___4___

3.

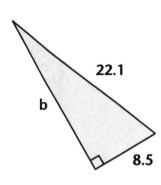

b = ___20.4___

4.

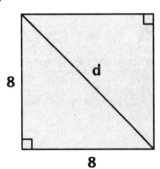

d = ___$8\sqrt{2}$ or ≈ 11.31___

5.

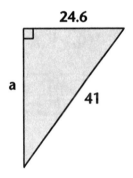

a = ___32.8___

6.

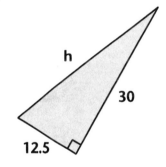

h = ___32.5___

7.

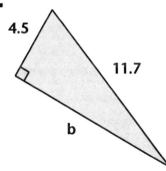

b = ___10.8___

8.

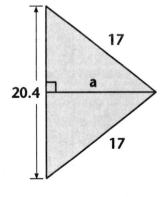

a = ___13.6___

9.

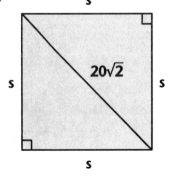

s = ___19.99998 ≈ 20___

SHORT STROKES & SQUARE ROOTS

Use your calculator to reach the target numbers. The catch? Do it with the **least** number of keystrokes and use at least one $\boxed{\sqrt{}}$. Answers may vary.

Digits to Use	Sequence	Target Number
1. 2,5	2 5 √	5.
2. 1,7	1 7 − 1 = √	4.
3. 0,3,7	3 7 0 − 3 = = = √	19.
4. 7,8	8 8 − 7 = √	9.
5. 1,6,7	1 1 7 + 6 − 1 = = √	11.
6. 8	8 ÷ 8 = √ ÷ 8 =	0.125
7. 0,4,9	9 0 0 √ + 4 √ =	32.
8. 1,2,6	2 6 − 1 = √ ÷ 2 =	2.5
9. 4	4 √ ÷ 4 = =	0.125
10. 0,2,7	2 0 7 − 7 − 2 = = √	14.

CHEERLEADER MATH

Complete each equation. Each solution matches with a letter. Put the matching letters in the spaces below to finish the cheer.

1. $21 \times (13 + 15 \times 9) - 52 \times 47 = ?$ **A**

2. $(33 \times 22 - 47) - 323 \div 17 = ?$ **C**

3. $5 \times 5 \times 5 + 13 \times 18 = ?$ **T**

4. $1539 \div 19 + 22 \times 18 = ?$ **L**

5. $23 \times 23 + 13 \times 17 = ?$ **A**

6. $8 \times (3 \times 17 + 14) = ?$ **L**

7. $871 \div 13 + 17 \times 17 = ?$ **U**

8. $(73 \times 3 + 17) \times (573 \div 191) = ?$ **C**

9. $79 \times 19 - 26 \times 41 = ?$ **E**

"Two, four, six, eight, I know how to

C A L C U L A T E ."

708 750 477 660 356 520 664 359 435

LESSON HELPERS

Lesson helper for:
WORD NAMES
See page 1

OBJECTIVES

Students recognize numbers from word names.

Procedures for Use

Use this activity when working with word names for numbers up to 999.

A skill developed early in the primary mathematics curriculum is the translation between word and numeral forms of numbers. Before using the activity sheet, use the Basic Overhead calculator or flash cards to introduce the lesson. Show the word "one hundred, twenty-three" on a large flash card or an overhead projector. Ask class, "This is a word name for what number?" Key in 123 on the overhead calculator. Have students key in 123 on their calculators. Make sure that students clear the display before going to the next example. Prepare a large square from oaktag with [ON/C] on it. Hold this up at this time. Tell class to press this key on their calculators. Using this technique, you will be sure they all are ready for the next example. Since no [=] key is pressed after the 123 is entered, an error buildup will occur if you attempt to enter a new number.

You need to have students practice keying in large numbers. Numbers of two or more digits are entered exactly as if they were being written with a pencil on paper. For 135, press 1, then 3, then 5. The 1 will float to the hundreds' place and the 3 to the tens' place.

Extensions

- Provide additional practice with three-digit numbers.
- Show words on the overhead projector or flash card. Have students take turns keying in the numbers on the Basic Overhead calculator.
- Depending on the ability level of students, you may want to extend the activity to four-digit numbers.
- Show numbers on the Basic Overhead calculator; have students write the word names.

Lesson helper for:
KNOW YOUR PLACE (VALUE)
See page 2

OBJECTIVES

Students translate place value expressed in words into numerals.

Procedures for Use

Use this activity after you extend place value to 999.

Recognizing and understanding place value are fundamental to the development of number sense. Students must be able to change words indicating place value into numerals.

Use oaktag cards or the overhead projector to show words expressing ones and tens. Do several examples using The Educator Basic Overhead calculator. Have students come to the projector and key in the numbers for each of the set of words in hundreds, tens and ones.

Use the activity sheet. Be sure that students clear their displays before each new example. Remind students that for two-digit and three-digit numbers, they are to be keyed in just as if they were writing them with pencil and paper.

Extensions

- Depending on the ability level of the students, extend to thousands.
- Key in numbers on The Educator Basic Overhead calculator. Have students write words showing hundreds, tens and ones; for example, for 327, students would write "3 hundreds, 2 tens, 7 ones."
- Challenge students by presenting words in non-standard form, such as "4 ones, 6 hundreds, and 2 tens" for 624.
- Provide examples with open-ended answers, such as, "Key in a number between 3 hundreds and 3 hundreds, 7 tens."

Lesson helper for:

WHAT'S THE COUNT?
See page 3

OBJECTIVES

Students count objects, key in numerals into their calculators, and record the displays on their activity sheets.

Procedures for Use

The relationship between telling "how many?" and writing a representation of the number that tells how many is an important skill learned in the primary grades. Equally important is to be able to key in the number representation on a calculator. Set up the activity by using the overhead projector. Place counters on the screen of the overhead projector. Ask students to tell how many counters are shown. Have them key in the number on their calculators. Reinforce the procedure by keying in the number on the Basic Overhead calculator. Repeat placing different numbers of counters on the overhead screen several times before using the activity sheet. Help students develop number sense by placing a number of counters, say 12 of them, in a random arrangement, then in two rows of six, or three rows of four. Beginning relationships between repeated addition and the operation of multiplication start with activities like this one.

Extensions

- Extend the activity using larger numbers of objects.
- Reverse the process. Key in number on the Basic Overhead calculator. Have students arrange the appropriate number of objects at their desks or tables.

Lesson helper for:

COUNT THE BUGS
See page 4

OBJECTIVES

Students count objects and write an addition sequence based on the number of objects to be counted.

Procedures for Use

Use this activity when you introduce combining three addends. Focus on the one-to-one correspondence between the number of bugs to be counted and the numbers to be added. Model several examples using counters on the overhead projector screen. For a set of 12 bugs or counters, students would write the numeral 12. Using a calculator, students would press a 1 then a 2. Repeat this process several times. Make sure students understand to record the final display for each sequence;

i.e., the display that results from pressing the =| key. Many students will "count on" beginning with the first addend. This is fine, but with larger numbers of objects, this procedure is cumbersome. For problem 1, you want to encourage thinking "twelve" plus "two" is "fourteen" and one more is "fifteen."

Reverse the process for greater understanding. Using the overhead projector or the chalkboard, give the students addition problems with three addends. Using counters or another manipulative, students must match each addend number with the appropriate number of counters. On the activity sheet, problems 6 and 7 utilize this method. Who can draw the best looking bugs?

Obviously, for more able students, activities such as this one may be a mental-math activity and you should encourage this thinking. But in a developmental lesson you want to be certain students can model the appropriate paper and pencil addition problem and calculator sequence.

Extensions

- Extend the activity using four and five addends.
- Provide examples in which the sums are 10 and multiples of 10's so students receive practice with use of 0 as a placeholder.
- Follow up the activity by having students draw three or more sets of objects to be counted and provide the corresponding addition problem.
- Show students that the order of the three addends makes no difference in the final sum; i.e., $3 + 5 + 2 = 2 + 5 + 3 = 5 + 3 + 2$, etc.

Lesson helper for:

TALLY TIME
See page 5

OBJECTIVES

Students count tally marks and key in the number of marks on their calculators.

Procedures for Use

Counting tally marks is one of the counting skills included in the primary mathematics curriculum. Use calculators and combine this skill with recording displays representing the number of tally marks. This is one more opportunity to build young students' confidence using technology.

Use manipulatives before distributing the activity sheet. Have students count objects and show them the convention of keeping tallies; i.e., tallies are grouped by fives and the fifth member of a group of five is written on the diagonal. This can be shown dramatically by showing 27 tallies of single strokes next to a recording of 27 tallies grouped by fives in the standard way. Which is easier to read? This is a good number sense activity-follow up the above activity by placing counters on the overhead in random fashion and again in groups of fives. This type of activity provides students with a foundation for the later study of multiplication.

Notice that students must clear each display before going to the next problem. Each answer must be cleared by pressing the [ON/C] key, otherwise an error will occur. Since no [=] key has been pressed in simply recording a number, if a second number is keyed in it will be affixed to the first number. Make sure students understand why the display must be cleared.

Extensions

- Do the same thing many times-such as bring your hand down on the desk. Students use tallies to keep track of the number of times you bring your hand down. Do several times, speeding up each time. Compare results.
- Do experiments with students and extend the activity to constructing charts and graphs of the experiments. Make tallies of the number of people who pass by the room in a 10-minute between-class period. Look out the window—make tallies of the number of cars that pass by the school in a 10-minute period.

Lesson helper for:
THE WAY HOME
See page 6

OBJECTIVES
Students follow directions and key in sequences.

Procedures for Use

Make sure students understand the directions. Point out that after the directions on the second sign are followed, "press [+][6]," each new operation will process the previous operation. Students may want to press the [=] key each time, but it is not necessary. This works because only additions and subtractions are being used.

Have students compare starting numbers and answers. There is good discovery work here; e.g., 12 is 5 more than 7, the final display, 37 is 5 more than 32. Use the activity sheet to generate additional problems. Replace the starting number with 4, 19, 0, etc. Ask questions like "If you replace a starting number with a larger starting number, will the number Mary takes home be larger or smaller than the previous number she took home?" Do

the same thing with a smaller starting number. These explorations help to develop number sense.

Extensions

- Have students generate their own set of road signs with similar directions. Share these student problems with the class.
- For higher-ability students: Compare results from each sequence with a shorter sequence; e.g., for 7, use [+][2][5][=]. Notice that the result, 32 is the same. (+6, –3, +11, +16, and –5 is the same as a single operation of +25). More explorations!
- Here's an opportunity for problem solving. Provide a take-home number; have students try to determine the start number. Some students will randomly try numbers. A successful strategy is to work backwards; but don't tell your students, let them figure it out.

Lesson helper for:
CLEAR SAILING
See page 7

OBJECTIVES
Students learn how to clear incorrect number entries.

Procedures for Use

Primary students make mistakes; maybe just a few. At any rate, they can learn how to use the [ON/C] key to correct their errors.

Many of the activities in this book use the [ON/C] key to clear displays.

The [ON/C] key has no effect on the memory. It is a dual-function key. Pressed once after a numerical entry, it will clear that number. Pressed twice, it will clear the entire display.

Explain to students that the key is used like an eraser when you make a mistake. You can model the use of the key by doing an addition on the chalkboard, erasing one of the addends, replacing it with another addend and then completing the addition.

Set up the activity by using the Basic Overhead calculator. Have students key in the same sequence that you use. Key in [2][+][5] and stop at this point. The 5 is in the display. Tell students that you made a mistake, you wanted to add 4 to the 2. Press the [ON/C] key. The display shows a 0. The 5 was erased. Now press [4][=] and the display reads 6, the sum of 2 and 4. Do several more to ensure that students understand how to clear a numerical entry.

Ask students to key in this sequence: [2][+][3][ON/C]

[ON/C] [1] [+] [7] [=]. Their displays will read 8, the sum of 1 and 7. Pressing the key twice clears the display, so everything before these keys is cleared.

Ask the students to try to do each problem without the use of the TI-108. After they guess the display, they then key in the sequence. Be sure the students see that some of the sequences take up two lines.

Extension

- Provide additional examples where students guess the final displays before using calculators.

Lesson helper for:
SNAKE THE SEQUENCES
See page 8

OBJECTIVES

Students complete a series of addition and subtraction sequences to reach a final display.

Procedures for Use

This activity sheet reinforces sequencing skills; i.e., the students merely key in numbers and record their final displays. But if you want students to become proficient using calculators, then practice activities such as this one are necessary.

Make sure students understand the directions. As they press each [=] key, the number in the display is used for the next part of the sequence trail. For problem 1, when the first [=] key is pressed, a 6 appears in the display. Students then press [−] [3] [=]. In doing a series of calculations, students may be used to clearing their displays, so they start with a display of 0. Or else, they do not clear and key in a new number to be added to or subtracted from. Here, each part of the trail is dependent on the previous part of the trail.

Extensions

- Use larger numbers. A convention used in this book is to include two sequence "boxes" for two-digit numbers. If you use two-digit numbers, use this convention or do not "box" in numbers when you are indicating a sequence.
- For higher-ability students, assign the task of creating a sequence trail similar to the activity sheet's trails. See who can make the longest trail. Check for accuracy.
- For students having difficulty with the activity, use counters; for problem 1, lay out 4 counters, lay out 2 more, that's 6. Now, let's take away 3 counters, that's 3, etc.

Lesson helper for:
A DOG RIDDLE
See page 9

OBJECTIVES

Students solve a riddle by finding missing numbers in addition and subtraction sequences.

Procedures for Use

Who said you can't have fun in a math class? Students engage in problem solving in this activity.

Either by "guess and check," using number sense, or understanding inverse relationships, students find missing numbers in addition and subtraction sequences.

Work through problem 1 with the class to see if they understand how to match up the display with the code to solve the riddle. For problem 1, the missing addend is 7. Look at the chart. The number 7 matches up with the letter A. So the A is placed in the blank over problem 1 in the phrase.

Use counters for those students who are having difficulty with finding missing numbers in addition or subtraction sequences.

For problem 1, lay out 15 counters on the overhead screen. Have a student lay out the number of counters to be added to 15 to get 22.

Extensions

- Students enjoy riddles. Have a class project involving making a riddle activity similar to this one. Help the students decide on a riddle, make up the sequences, code, etc. Present your activity to another class to solve.
- Have students write about their class riddle activity.

Lesson helper for:
THE COVER-UP RIDDLE
See page 10

OBJECTIVES

Students add numbers by keying in addition sequences.

Students follow directions to solve a riddle.

Procedures for Use

This is a straightforward activity in that students simply key in sequences and then record the displays. It is also devoid of a context setting. But for students to gain confidence using calculators to solve problems and to work with larger numbers later in using mathematics, then at this level they need ample practice in keying in sequences.

Make sure students understand the directions. For example, the first display is 19, there's an A next to the first display. So, below in the incomplete sentence, the A is placed in the blank over the number, 19. There are eight blanks and eight displays. Thus, if the activity is successfully completed, students should have the answer to the question, "What is Mary hiding?"

Extensions

- Make up additional "riddles" for the students to solve.
- As a class activity, create a "riddle." Give it to other teachers for their classes to solve.

Lesson helper for:
HARVEST THE NUMBERS
See page 11

OBJECTIVES

Students engage in problem solving using digits to complete sequences.

Students use basic addition and subtraction facts.

Students use higher-order thinking skills.

Procedures for Use

Help students get started on this activity. They have to "pick" digits from the tree and complete the sequences. The "guess-and-check" strategy will be used often in working through the activity. It's not as easy as it looks. For example, in problem 1, students may think that 8 and 6 are the choices; their sum is 14. But the pair 9 and 5 also sum to 14. Which pair to use? That's the purpose of the activity, to figure out the right choices!

Here's a hint for you; but don't tell your students, let them explore! Don't start at the beginning. Go through the sequences doing those where there are no choices. Do these first and everything will fall in place.

Make sure students understand that they are to use each of the digits one time only. Also, be sure they see that in some of the sequences two digits are to be used to form two-digit numbers. For example, in problem 5, a 2 and a 4 need to be "picked" from the tree to name the number 24.

Encourage students to discuss how they did the activity. This type of activity helps to develop logical thinking. Young students may not be used to a "guess-and-check" approach. Review both successful and non-successful approaches.

Extensions

- Provide additional activities using a "guess-and-check" problem-solving strategy and use of

higher-order thinking skills. Make up five sequences, involving addition and subtraction. Erase numbers from the sequences and put in a "tree" for the students to "pick."

Lesson helper for:
COIN VALUES
See page 12

OBJECTIVES

Students use calculators to record the value of pennies, nickels and dimes.

Procedures for Use

Use this activity when introducing the value of a dime. Students use the calculator to record the value of the coins. Most students will use mental math, but with the inclusion of the dime, some primary students may need the calculator to sum the value of the coins.

Since no ⬚= key is used on the sheet, the ⬚ON/C key must be pressed between examples, otherwise there will be an error buildup.

Use real coins to set up the activity. Make sure the students understand the difference between the number of coins and the value of coins.

Extensions

- Use more coins of each type.
- Students develop number sense with activities such as this one. Ask students which examples are easier to tell "How much?" Those where the coins are arranged by type or those where the coins are arranged in a mixed order?
- Reverse the process, give students values of coins and ask for combinations of coins with that value.
- Try this: use exactly five coins (pennies, nickels, dimes) for a value of
  - a) 36 cents   (3 dimes, 1 nickel, 1 penny)
  - b) 14 cents   (1 dime, 4 pennies)
  - c) 22 cents   (1 dime, 2 nickels, 2 pennies)

Lesson helper for:
MORE COIN VALUES
See page 13

OBJECTIVES

Students use calculators to record the value of coins.

Students use decimal notation to record the value of coins.

Procedures for Use

Use this activity when working with the value of pennies, nickels, dimes and quarters. Also, at this level you want students to use decimal notation for dollars and cents.

The objective here is to record money values. Most students figure out the value of the coins mentally, then key in the value and record it.

Also notice that no ⊟ key is used on the sheet, so the ON/C key must be pressed between examples; otherwise there will be an error buildup. By this time, students should know this and the ON/C key is not included on the activity sheet.

Use real coins to set up the activity. Make sure students understand the difference between the number of coins and the value of the coins.

For problem 1, you want a display of $0.3I$ representing $.31. Notice that the first two problems illustrate that the order of the coins does not change their value. When students solve a word problem, they need to label their answer. Practice having students interpret their displays; e.g., a display of $I.25$ represents $1.25. Students are able to key in a 0 in the hundredths place as in $I.50$ for $1.50 but the 0 will not be displayed as a result of a computation; for example, for 2 items at $.75, students key in ②⊠⦁⑦⑤⊟. The display will read $I.5$.

The last five problems use a table without pictures of coins. At this level, students will add the values of the coins. For problem 6, 0.25 + 0.25 + 0.10 + 0.10 + 0.10 + 0.05 + 0.01 + 0.01 = 0.87.

Extensions

- Depending on the ability level of the students, use more coins.
- Reverse the process. Use the Basic Overhead calculator and give students a display; for example, $I.2$. "How much money is this?" ($1.20) "Can you give me 6 coins with a value of $1.20?" If the discussion is limited to coins, no dollar bills and no half-dollar coins, then the only answer is 4 quarters and 2 dimes. This extension provides rich exploration for students.

Lesson helper for:
PRICE TAGS
See page 14

OBJECTIVES
Students show money amounts in displays and interpret displays as dollars and cents.

Procedures for Use

This is a basic but necessary activity. Students in grades 2 and 3 work with U.S. currency. When using calculators, it is important to be able to enter money amounts and interpret money displays.

Once students begin working with dollars and cents, cents are represented as part of a dollar; e.g., 25¢ is written as $.25. Similarly, 50¢ is written as $.50. When working with money, the "0" in the hundredths place is shown. Students can key in .50 for $.50; press ⦁⑤⓪. These non-significant zeroes can be entered, but will not be shown as a result of a computation. If 2 items are bought at $1.25 each, press the sequence: ②⊠①⦁②⑤⊟. See, the display reads 2.5. Students have to be taught that this represents $2.50.

Use the Basic Overhead calculator to introduce the activity. You want to be sure students can enter cents as dollars and cents and interpret displays as dollars and cents. Hold up flash cards with money amounts and have students come to the overhead and key in the display. Also, show a display and have students write the corresponding "dollars and cents" representation.

This basic work is fundamental to success in using calculators with money problems in the elementary curriculum. We sometimes assume certain things are obvious and that simply is not true.

For the first half of the activity, students are to key in money as parts of dollars and not as pennies; e.g., for 39¢, the desired display is 0.39.

Extensions

- Use newspaper advertisements of food prices to generate additional practice.
- Do some basic computations where the displays will give answers with no zero in the hundredths place; e.g., a display of 1.2 written with pencil and paper is interpreted as $1.20.

Lesson helper for:
OPERATION FILL IN
See page 15

OBJECTIVES
Students use number sense and basic-skills knowledge to supply missing addition and subtraction signs to key sequences.

Procedures for Use

At the primary level, students have worked only with the operations of addition and subtraction. Review the directions prior to use. Allow students to use their own strategies to find the missing operations for each sequence. If students are having difficulty, provide one of the two operations and make a slower transition to sequences with two missing operations. Another strategy is to model with counters, adding on or subtracting counters until the desired result is obtained.

Extensions

- Use larger numbers.
- Eliminate the final displays and make the activity more open-ended. For problem 1, possible whole number answers are 9 (+, +) and 7 (–, +). Using (–, –) would yield a negative number (–5) which is not a whole number.

Lesson helper for:
STICK SUMS
See page 16

OBJECTIVES

Students solve problems involving measurement.

Students measure with a customary ruler.

Students use addition facts.

Students use higher-order thinking skills.

Procedures for Use

This activity embodies many of the goals of elementary mathematics. It integrates calculator use in a problem-solving setting.

Use this activity with cooperative-learning groups. Before the groups start work, review the directions. Distribute customary rulers.

Students measure the lengths of the sticks. They then have to follow the directions and find combined lengths of sticks. Emphasize that they must find the desired lengths and the correct number of sticks. It is implied that the sticks are laid end to end with no overlap. There are duplicates of these sticks in the "factory." Thus, three F sticks could be used for a length of 15 inches.

After a specified time has passed, have groups report on their findings.

Extensions

- Have students write about the activity.
- Have students add additional sticks and lengths to the "factory" and create more problems.
- Do a similar activity using metric lengths (centimeters).

Lesson helper for:
DITTO THE DIGITS
See page 17

OBJECTIVES

Students find missing numbers in addition and subtraction sequences.

Students use higher-order thinking skills.

Procedures for Use

Read the directions with your students. There's some good number-sense work here. At first, it looks open-ended, but it's not. Work with the class on the first one before letting them loose on the activity. For problem 1, you must find two numbers whose sum is 8. But, the two addends must be the same number. So, the only choice is 4 (4 + 4 = 8).

In other cases, two of the same digit have to be combined to form a number, as in the two-digit number, 11. You may want to review how the ten digits are used to form two-digit numbers. These sequences provide rich exploration using calculators.

Some of the sequences indicate repeated addition and lay a foundation for later work with multiplication.

Extensions

- If you have introduced larger two-digit numbers and three-digit numbers, you can extend this activity and make it more challenging;
  e.g., _ _ _ + _ _ + _ = 123
  (Use a 1 in each space).

Lesson helper for:
HIT THE TARGET
See page 18

OBJECTIVES

Students use the constant feature of the TI-108 to reach goal numbers.

Students use mental math and number-sense skills.

Procedures for Use

This activity sheet does not contain enough directions for the students to begin it independently; thus, your active involvement in setting up the activity is vital. The TI-108 will constantly add the second number of a sum if the ⊟ key is continually pressed. For example, 2 ⊞ 1 ⊟ ⊟ ⊟ ⊟ will yield displays of 3, 4, 5, and 6 respectively. This feature is used in here to engage students in a number-sense activity. The first one is done for the students. The target number 15 is reached, 3 + 3 + 3 + 3 + 3 = 15. For the other problems, encourage students to guess whether they will hit the target number before they press the ⊟ key. They then pencil in "Yes" or "No." Space is provided for students to indicate the correct number of ⊟ keys for the target numbers that can be reached. Guesses made and entered in the last column may have to be revised after students explore pressing the ⊟ key.

Ideas about odd and even numbers and repeated addition are explored here. Ask students to explain their answers.

Extensions

- Use larger numbers as the target numbers.
- Have students make up sequences and target numbers.
- Here's a good problem-solving extension: provide a target number that can be "reached;" then provide one of the two addends in the original sum–students need to find the other addend.
  For example:
  3 ⊞ __ ⊟ ⊟ ⊟ ⊟ Target number: 11
  (answer is 2)
  2 ⊞ __ ⊟ ⊟ ⊟ ⊟ Target number: 22
  (answer is 5)
  __ ⊞ 7 ⊟ ⊟ ⊟ Target number: 36
  (answer is 8)
- Extend the activity to subtraction:
  24 ⊟ 2 with a target number of 10; (Yes, ⊟ ⊟
  ⊟ ⊟ ⊟ ⊟ ⊟)
  18 ⊟ 3 with a target number of 8; (No)
  50 ⊟ 10 with a target number of 0; (Yes, ⊟ ⊟
  ⊟ ⊟ ⊟)

Lesson helper for:
SHAPE SHOPPING
See page 19

OBJECTIVES

Students use addition to solve problems involving costs of shapes.

Procedures for Use

At the primary level, your students will solve these problems using addition. Discuss the names of the shapes; this is a good opportunity to develop vocabulary. Make sure students understand the prices of the different shapes. For problem 1, encourage students to use mental math. For the second problem, you want students to see 6 + 6 + 8. Some students will see the answer to problem 3 as being 8 more than the answer to problem 2. Discuss these observations; they help develop number sense. Compare the result in problem 3 with the result in problem 1. Start developing the concepts of

"doubles" and "twice as much." For problems 7 and 8, the answers are the same. Make sure students see that regardless of the order, the value of the shapes is the same. Encourage students to think, "two rectangles and three circles."

Extensions

- Have students make up their own problems involving these shapes.
- For a challenge, give a total cost, and have students determine possible answers; e.g., "If you spent 48¢, what shapes could you have bought?" These open-ended activities provide a great problem-solving environment.
- For additional practice, change the price structure of the shapes.
- Add other shapes and prices.

Lesson helper for:
THANKS FOR THE MEMORIES
See page 20

OBJECTIVES

Students are introduced to the memory keys on the TI-108 calculator.

Students use the memory keys to add and subtract numbers.

Procedures for Use

Students in the early grades have experiences only with the operations of addition and subtraction. They cannot be expected to work with consumer problems involving the operation of multiplication and, while doing, utilize the power of the calculator's memory keys. But they can learn how to use the three keys that access memory functions to add and subtract numbers.

Use this activity sheet to introduce the memory keys. Demonstrate with the Basic Overhead calculator by pointing to the three keys you will be using in the lesson. Do problem 1 with the class. Key in 3. Press [M+]. As soon as the [M+] key is pressed, an M appears in the top left corner of the display. Make sure the students understand that the M is the memory indicator and signifies that something (in this case, 3) has been saved. Though not necessary, now press the [ON/C] key, clearing the display. The display shows 0 and the memory indicator, M. Now, press the [MRC] key and, presto, there's the 3. Pressing [MRC] one time performs the R in [MRC]; it recalls or brings the contents of the memory to the display. Students should record a 3 in the display box for problem 1 on their activity sheet. Although not directed on the activity sheet, have students press the [MRC] key again. If it is pressed twice, the memory is cleared, the C (for *Clear*) is performed. Students will argue with you here. They'll tell you that you still have the 3. Point out that the memory indicator is no longer in the display indicating that the memory has been cleared. What happens is that when the memory is cleared, its content, the 3, is brought to the display. Before continuing with the activity sheet, provide additional examples for students to practice using the memory keys. Introduce the [M−] key in the same fashion. Remember that pressing [M−] subtracts the display number from the number in memory.

Since the last key pressed is [MRC] pressing it again will clear the memory. Press [ON/C] so students will begin each new sequence with a "0" in the display.

Primary grade students can learn how to use the features of a calculator. You must introduce the special keys slowly and give your students plenty of time to explore.

Extension
- Add and subtract larger numbers using the [M+] and [M−] keys.

Lesson helper for:
ADDITION TRAIN
See page 21

OBJECTIVES
Students engage in problem solving by finding two or more numbers for designated sums.

Students add three-digit numbers with regrouping with up to four-digit sums.

Procedures for Use
This activity is indicative of many activities which, with a slight shift in emphasis, can become effective problem-solving experiences for young students. Many times students are given worksheets to "practice" computational skills. These worksheets often are devoid of any problem solving. More problem-solving activities are needed in the early grades-use this approach; your students will enjoy the mathematics you teach them.

Review the directions with your students. They are given fourteen three-digit numbers from which to use in addition problems.

The shift in emphasis involves giving students the sums and they have to pick out the addends which yield the sums.

The availability of the calculator allows students to explore many combinations in a "guess-and-verify" search for the two, three, or four numbers which will satisfy the

conditions. Some students will immediately start pressing buttons. Others will use estimation skills and good number sense to limit the possibilities and then use the calculator to verify their guesses. Students will look at sums of unit digits to further limit possibilities. All of the numbers will not be used in the activity.

This type of activity provides a good opportunity for students to discuss their work. Have students explain their thinking.

Extensions
- Use the same set of numbers to make up more sums.
- Try 5 addends.
- For extended work with addition, use four-digit numbers for sums to five digits.

Lesson helper for:
SUM PATHS
See page 22

OBJECTIVES
Students add numbers to reach target numbers.

Procedures for Use
At first glance, this looks like a difficult activity. It involves some good old "number crunching." You may be surprised how quickly some of your students reach the target numbers.

Review the directions with students. For each puzzle, students start with the number in the START box. Legal moves involve down, over, and up moves. No diagonal moves are permitted. You may want to review the meaning of "diagonal." The instruction, "You cannot cross your path." implies that the same number cannot be used more than one time. As students make a path, they add the numbers in the boxes. The object is to reach the target sum.

Have students work in cooperative groups. Many students will use mental math to work through the first puzzle and perhaps, the second one. As the puzzles increase in difficulty, the advantage of having a calculator becomes apparent.

One strategy students quickly pick up is that the number in the box directly above the target number will be included in the path. Others will find the sum of all sixteen numbers in the puzzle and then selectively subtract numbers till they near the target number. In cooperative groups students will portion out different paths to members of the group to test.

Have students discuss their work after all paths are determined. This dialogue is an important part of this activity.

Extensions

- Make additional Sum Paths for the class to solve.
- Use larger numbers.
- Have students try to create Sum Paths; start with a 3 x 3 puzzle using single-digit numbers. Have those who create trails write a report on their Path Projects.

Lesson helper for:
THE MATH MACHINE
See page 23

OBJECTIVES

Students use the calculator as a function machine and solve problems involving subtraction.

Procedures for Use

Use this activity after teaching subtraction. In this activity, students observe a machine that takes two numbers, does something to them, and produces a single number. What is the machine doing?

That is what students have to discover in the first part of the activity. They will tell you that the machine is subtracting. Continue the discussion and ask what is similar about all the pairs that go into the machine. It is important that students see that for each pair the first number is always larger than or equal to the second number. Give students more pairs of numbers till they are all sure they know what the machine is doing.

The calculator can be used as a function machine, that is, two numbers go in, you do some operation, and one number is produced in the display. You can do this with pairs of numbers using the Basic Overhead calculator. Ask for two numbers. Key in the first number, press the addition key but do not let the students see you press the addition key, key in the second number, and press ⌑. Do for other pairs till someone generalizes. Once students learn multiplication, you can combine operations for your "mystery machine."

There are opportunities here for higher-order thinking. For some of the problems, students are given the output number and must supply one of the input numbers. Look at the last problem. This is open-ended, any pair of numbers with a difference of 37 will work, as long as the first one is the larger of the two numbers; 37 and 0, 38 and 1, 39 and 2, etc. Some of your students will be creative here, with pairs of numbers of four and five digits.

Extensions

- Provide additional pairs for this "mystery machine." Give examples with an input number missing, or

give them the output number with both input numbers missing.
- You can make more involved rules; for example, given a pair of numbers, double the first and add the second. For rules which involve the operation of subtraction or later, division, make sure the result will be a whole number.

Lesson helper for:
DISPLAY THE WORDS
See page 24

OBJECTIVES

Students add and subtract three- and four-digit numbers with their calculators and form upside-down "words" in their displays.

Procedures for Use

This one needs explaining. Again, directions on the activity are purposely sparse because you want to lead the activity at the onset. Once students understand and complete the activity, there are several extensions for students to explore.

While this may seem corny, it is a useful type of activity because it is self-checking. Furthermore, it provides a wealth of mathematics as students attempt to create words from use of their TI-108s.

Certain electronic digits in a display when turned upside down resemble certain letters. For example, key in 5508. Turn the calculator upside down. Now look at the display; do you see the word **BOSS**? O.K., so it is corny but it works! Your students will have fun and will get involved in an activity matching up number answers and upside-down "words."

Students do the computations using their calculators. A space is provided for the number answer and the "word" answer. Then they have to put the "word" in the blank space in the sentence in which it seems most appropriate.

Set up the activity with use of the Basic Overhead calculator. Key in the number 3507. Turn the overhead calculator upside down on the stage of the overhead projector. There's the word **LOSE**. In some cases, you will be mixing upper and lower-case letters, a small price to pay for a good math lesson!

Extensions

- Have the class determine those digits that produce "letters."
- Give students a "word" and have them make up an addition or a subtraction problem that will produce the "word." This is not as easy as it looks. Obviously,

the activity is limited to the vocabulary of young students.
- Determine if any student's name can be made into a math problem producing a "word." It helps to have someone named Bob in your class.

Lesson helper for:

AN OCEAN RIDDLE
See page 25

OBJECTIVES

Students multiply numbers by keying in sequences.
Students follow directions to solve a riddle.

Procedures for Use

This is a straightforward activity in that students simply key in sequences and then record the displays. It is also devoid of a context setting. But – for students to gain confidence using calculators to solve problems and to work with larger numbers later in using mathematics, then at this level they need ample practice in keying in sequences.

Make sure students understand the directions. For example, the first display is 24; there is an I next to the first display. So, below in the incomplete phrase, the I is placed in the blank over the number, 24. There are nine blanks and nine displays. Thus, if the activity is successfully completed, students should have the answer to the riddle.

Extensions
- Make up additional riddles for the students to solve.
- As a class activity, create a riddle. Give it to other teachers for their classes to solve.
- Ask students to write about the riddle activity.

Lesson helper for:

AND THE NUMBER LEFT IS...
See page 26

OBJECTIVES

Students engage in problem solving using knowledge of multiplication facts and higher-order thinking skills.

Procedures for Use

Set up the lesson using a similar procedure on the chalkboard or overhead projector. Make sure students understand the directions. What's bothersome to students is that there may be more than one answer for each example. Which one to pick? A trial-and-error method needs to be used. Make sure students are using a pencil with an eraser. There will be blind alleys encountered as they find the correct pairs for each example. Each number can be used only one time!

Many students will use mental math as they go through the examples using the calculator to verify their choices. Others will randomly pick numbers and key them into the calculator. Let students use whatever method they wish. They will quickly discover the most efficient strategy.

This is a good activity to use with cooperative-learning groups. Permit students to explain their methods after the activity is completed.

Extensions
- Extend activity using larger numbers. How do you put one of these together? Write down four multiplication equations. Throw in an extra number. Put all nine numbers, jumbled up, in the box, and presto, you have a problem to solve.
- Create a problem using three factors.

Lesson helper for:

PRODUCT PATHS
See page 27

OBJECTIVES

Students multiply numbers to reach target numbers.

Procedures for Use

Like a previous activity, SUM PATHS, this looks like a difficult activity. It, too, involves some good old "number crunching." You may be surprised how quickly some of your students reach the target numbers.

Review the directions with students. For each puzzle, students start with the number in the START box. Legal moves involve down, over, and up moves. No diagonal moves are permitted. You may want to review the meaning of diagonal. The instruction, "You cannot cross your path." implies that the same number cannot be used more than one time. As students make a path, they multiply the numbers in the boxes. The object is to reach the target product.

Have students work in cooperative groups. Many students will use mental math to work through parts of the puzzles and use estimation skills. Knowledge of factors and multiples will be used. There are boxes with 0 in them which should assist students in limiting path choices. Students will also use the 1 factors to limit the size of the product.

One strategy students quickly pick up is that the number in the box directly above the target number will be included in the path. Students will learn to not use the larger numbers as factors because the final products will be too large. In cooperative groups students will portion out different paths to members of the group to test.

Have students discuss their work after all paths are determined. This dialogue is an important part of this activity.

Extensions

- Use the same puzzles to name other path numbers.
- Make additional multiplication paths for the class to solve. Choose factors carefully so target numbers will not be too large.
- Have students try to create multiplication paths; start with a 3 x 3 puzzle using single-digit numbers. Have those who create paths write a report on their Path Projects.

Lesson helper for:
TARGET TOSS
See page 28

OBJECTIVES

Students use multiplication and division to determine factors of target numbers.

Procedures for Use

Use this after students have worked with multiplication and division.

You have to use your imagination here. Your students will have no trouble using their imaginations! Actually, you could make a game board, tape it to the chalkboard, and have students throw real bean bags at the board. The big difference is that with this activity it is assumed that all bean bags hit a number. Your students will not be that accurate. First check with your principal.

This embodies the type of activity for which the calculator is an excellent aid. Set up the game. As bean bags are "thrown" and hit numbers, the numbers are multiplied. Students are given the scores (products) and must determine which numbers are hit. Make sure students understand that they need to get the product with the correct number of bean bags. In some cases, they may get the right product but with the incorrect number of bags thrown. They will ask if you can hit the same number more than once. Let them discover that you must have multiple hits in some of the problems.

For three throws (problems 1 and 6), many students will use mental math. For the other throws, some students will multiply numbers randomly attempting to hit the score. Other students will use division, trying to "break down" the number into factors that match the numbers on the board. Others will notice that a product is even, so it can be divided by 2. Or, if a product does not end in a 0 or 5, then you cannot divide it by 5. There is a lot of math here!

Extensions

- Use other numbers and make up more game boards.
- Use more than 4 numbers to a board.
- Have students write about the activity. How did they feel about searching for the numbers?

Lesson helper for:
A WEATHER RIDDLE
See page 29

OBJECTIVES

Students solve a riddle by finding missing numbers in multiplication and division sequences.

Procedures for Use

Use this activity after students have had experiences with multiplication and division.

Who said you can't have fun in a math class? Students engage in problem solving in this activity. Either by "guess and check," using number sense, or understanding inverse relationships, students find missing numbers in multiplication and division sequences.

Explain the directions to students. Work through the first example with the class to see if they understand how to match up the display with the code to solve the riddle. The missing factor is 4. Look at the chart. The number 4 matches up with the letter R. So the R is placed in the blank over 1. in the phrase.

Extensions

- Students enjoy riddles. Have a class project involving making a riddle activity similar to this one. Help the students decide on a riddle, make up the sequences, code, etc. Present your activity to another class to solve.
- Have students write about their class riddle activity.

Lesson helper for:
SOLVE THE MYSTERIES
See page 30

OBJECTIVES

Students use clues about numbers to solve word mysteries.

Procedures for Use

Use this activity after all four operations have been taught. This is a challenging activity for students at this level; have them work in groups. Communication skills are important in the primary grades. Students read clues about mystery numbers and then try to identify the numbers.

Set up the activity by doing the first one together. This is a missing addend problem. "What number added to 57 will give you a sum of 103?" If students have trouble with this, use a simpler problem, such as "If you add me to 5, the sum is 9. Who am I?" Similar techniques with the other problems will help the students through the activity. Working backwards and using relationships between addition and subtraction, and multiplication and division are successful strategies to use. Review the difference in terminology like "multiply and then add" and "add and then multiply" and how the calculator processes operations.

Have students check their work by replacing the word "me" with the answer.

Extensions

- Have students create mystery stories.
- Have students act out the stories by reading them.
- Develop a bulletin board activity using the students' stories.

Lesson helper for:
FIND THE MATCHES
See page 31

OBJECTIVES

Students use mental math, number sense, and basic skills to match expressions.

Procedures to Use

This is one of those calculator activities which reinforces mental math. You want to use this as a timed activity. Prior to distributing the activity sheet, explain to the class that the objective is to find five matches as quickly as possible.

In the grid there are 24 expressions, twelve pairs of matching ones. Explain to students that they only have to find five of the matching pairs. Build up the activity as a game. "Ready, get set, go!" Students list their matches on the sheet. To keep track of the simplified expressions, instruct students to put the answers in the boxes; therefore, for A, students should write a 26 in the A box. Your students will not necessarily do the first one; they will jump around looking for the easier computations. You can either check individual students' matches as they complete the activity or wait till most of the class is finished. Record the time lapse for students on their papers.

Students who complete the activity successfully in the shortest time will use mental math and number sense. Other students who rely on the calculator will take the longest to complete the sheet. Make sure they under-stand that they do not have to do all 24 problems, but only find five matches. It would be rare for someone to do just ten problems to find the five matches.

Have students discuss the activity and explain the process they used to find their five matches. Insights into students' thinking will emerge. Use this timed format many times during the school year. It is an excellent way for students to learn the appropriate use of calculators.

Extensions

- Extend the discussion. "Who did the least number of problems to get five matches?" "Tell us what you did?" Without embarrassing students, you want students to see that, in many cases, it is quicker to use mental math rather than the calculator.
- If you create additional match games, include more problems which are more calculator appropriate for the level of your students. The objective here is to force students into using mental math and number-sense skills, but if you want to change the objective and have them use calculators for most of the problems, then make the computations more difficult.

Lesson helper for:
SCHOOL STORE SALE
See page 32

OBJECTIVES

Students combine multiplication and addition to solve money problems.

Procedures to Use

Use this activity after students have started work with multiplication. If students have worked with decimal notation for money, then they may use 0.25 for 25¢. In this activity, you want students to use multiplication and addition as opposed to stringing together all additions. Review the definition of multiplication as repeated addition.

If you have yet to teach students how to use the memory keys, students will have to write down the individual cost of items before finding each total cost.

Compare the results of examples 1. and 2. Students begin to develop number sense by seeing the relationship between these two examples. The second answer is twice the first answer. The number of pens and erasers were both doubled. Try other examples similar to this one.

Encourage students to use mental math where appropriate. For example 5., ask if it is necessary to key in 1 x 25.

Refer back to example 1., where students probably just added 39 + 6 not using the factors of 1.

Example 8. is the most important example on the activity sheet because of its open-ended nature. Allow students to work in groups at this point. Let all groups report on their "orders," reviewing the items purchased and the work of the students.

Extensions

- Add items to the store's "inventory" and create additional problems.
- Challenge students by starting them off with a $5 or $10 bill. Ask how much change they will get? The strategy here is to key in the starting amount first and then subtract each cost. The final display will represent the students' change.
- Ask students what was bought if $1.28 was spent. Answers may vary; one possibility is two notepads and two pens.

Lesson helper for:
REMEMBER ME
See page 33

OBJECTIVES
Students use memory keys to solve consumer problems.

Procedures for Use

This activity is for use when teaching students how to use the memory keys. Using the TI-108, it is necessary to use the memory keys to find sums and differences of products. This activity is to be used after multiplication has been covered and students have worked with U.S. money.

Review the use of the memory keys using the Basic Overhead Calculator. Then work through the first four problems with the students; make sure they understand each of the final displays.

Review the relationship between dollars and cents. If students have not used their calculators to do money problems, explain that the display will not show a non-significant 0. For $1.50, the display will read *1.5*.

Use cooperative groups to do problems 5–8. Have groups explain their work.

Extensions

- Have students write "money stories" complete with answers.
- Use newspaper advertisements to generate additional problems.

Lesson helper for:
FRUIT SHOPPING
See page 34

OBJECTIVES
Students determine total costs of orders at a fruit stand.

Procedures for Use

This is a busy looking activity sheet but just the type of activity for which the TI-108 was designed. Use this activity after students have learned to use all the features of the TI-108 and have covered multiplication and problems involving money.

Review the directions with your class. Make sure they understand the price structure for the various items; some items are sold by the pound, others by the pint, each, and several for a certain amount. Review the use of the symbol for pound.

Have some fun with your class and bring in from home some of the fruits used in the activity. Students in some areas of the country may not be familiar with all the different fruits used.

Space is provided for students to list the cost of individual items; you may want to require that they do, in fact, list these prices. Use M+ to sum costs of individual items and MRC to recall from memory the total cost of an order.

Be sure to allow time for students to discuss how they did their work.

Extensions

- Have students determine the correct change for each order by telling them how much money is given to the clerk for each order. For example, for order 1, if the clerk is given a $10 bill, how much change is due?
- Have students make up additional orders.
- Have students bring in newspaper advertisements from the food section of the local newspaper. Create additional activities, involving food purchases.
- Another type of extension involves giving students a total cost and having them try to determine what was purchased.

Lesson helper for:
PLACE VALUE CHECK
See page 35

OBJECTIVES
Students follow directions using place-value skills and knowledge of mathematics vocabulary.

Procedures for Use

Use this activity after covering place value to the millions' place. Students have to add large numbers but, of course, they will have their calculators to help them.

This type of activity requires students to use all the answers to arrive at a "final" answer. Make sure students understand that the number box contains twelve numbers-the commas are separating the periods in an individual number. Review vocabulary with students, three-digit numbers, smallest, largest, etc. Review place value also.

Students record the answers in the spaces provided. If all the answers are correct, after adding 3,674,873, they turn the calculator upside down. The electronic digits resemble letters and they should see a word that answers the question, "What do scuba divers wear?"

Extensions

- Use the same set of numbers to generate additional problems with "word" answers.
- Have students provide numbers that will yield "words."

Lesson helper for:
MORE SUM PATHS
See page 36

OBJECTIVES

Students add numbers to reach target numbers.

Procedures for Use

At first glance, this looks like a difficult activity. It involves some good old "number crunching." You may be surprised how quickly some of your students reach the target numbers.

Review the directions with students. For each puzzle, students start with the number in the "START" box. Legal moves involve down, over, and up moves. No diagonal moves are permitted. The instruction, "You cannot cross your path," implies that the same number cannot be used more than one time. As students make a path, they add the numbers in the boxes. The object is to reach the target sum.

Have students work in cooperative groups. Many students will use estimation skills to find a number close to the target number, then use their calculators to check their estimation.

One strategy students quickly pick up is that the number in the box directly above the target number will be included in the path. Others will find the sum of all sixteen numbers in the puzzle and then selectively subtract

numbers till they near the target number. In cooperative groups students will portion out different paths to members of the group to test.

Have students discuss their work after all paths are determined. This dialogue is an important part of this activity.

Extensions

- Make additional Sum Paths for the class to solve.
- Use larger numbers.
- Have students try to create Sum Paths; start with a 3 x 3 puzzle. Have those who create paths write a report on their Path Projects.

Lesson helper for:
PRODUCT SEARCH
See page 37

OBJECTIVES

Students choose from the ten digits to search for maximum and minimum products in multi-digit multiplications.

Procedures for Use

Use this activity after teaching multiplication of large numbers.

This activity embodies all the advantages of using calculators. Such searches would be cumbersome without the use of a calculator. It parallels many real-world applications in which exhaustive searches must be performed.

Review the directions with students. For the first problem, students are searching for the largest possible product of a three-digit multiplied by a one-digit number. A digit can be used only once per problem. 999 x 9 is not acceptable!

Organize your class into cooperative groups. Effective groups will partition work among members. The need to keep an organized list will become evident. Paper and pencil are still needed!

Many students will be convinced that the correct answer for the first one is 987 x 6; exploring different combinations will show them that this is not true. Students will discover patterns as they search for the largest or smallest products. Point out that some of the problems have an additional condition, such as "odd" or "even." This will provide an opportunity to use higher-order thinking skills.

Extensions

- Provide additional problems using multi-digit factors.
- Have students write a report or make a journal entry on the lesson.

Lesson helper for:
SEARCHING FOR PATTERNS
See page 38

OBJECTIVES

Students use mental math and higher-order thinking skills to find missing numbers in patterns.

Procedures for Use

This activity can be used anytime after students work with addition, subtraction, and multiplication with whole numbers. For many of the patterns, students will not need a calculator but will find all missing numbers using mental math. For other patterns, a good deal of thinking and exploring different hunches will be necessary and the calculator will be used exstensively in these explorations.

At this level, students will not be using algebra to explain their answers. To get from one number to the next one, students must apply the same "rule." For the first one, a student's explanation might be "You double each number to get the next one." For the third one, an acceptable explanation is "You double the number and add 2 to get the next one."

Make sure students understand that the same operation or operations must be performed each time to get to the next number. Students cannot change the "rule" in the middle of a pattern. There are more sophisticated explanations for the patterns, but at the middle school level the types of explanations as the above ones are acceptable.

Have some fun with your students. The last three patterns have non-traditional answers; the use of the calculator will be of little help. They do however involve opportunities to use higher-order thinking skills. Tell students that these are a little different. For pattern 13., each number in the pattern is obtained by squaring the counting numbers and reversing the digits. For the fourth number in the pattern, $4^2=16$, reverse the digits of 16 to get 61.

Extensions

- Show students how to use the features of the TI-108 to generate numbers in some of the patterns; e.g., for pattern 1., press 2 $\boxed{\times}$ 1 $\boxed{=}$ $\boxed{=}$ $\boxed{=}$; for pattern 2., press 3 $\boxed{\times}$ 1 $\boxed{=}$ $\boxed{=}$ $\boxed{=}$, etc.
- Have students generate patterns for the class to guess the "rule."

Lesson helper for:
ANOTHER MATH MACHINE
See page 39

OBJECTIVES

Students use the calculator as a function machine and solve problems involving multiplication and addition.

Procedures for Use

Use this activity after teaching addition and multiplication of whole numbers. In this activity, students observe a machine that takes two numbers, does something to them, and produces a single number. What is the machine doing?

That is what students have to discover in the first part of the activity. They will tell you that the machine is doubling the first number or multiplying it by 2 and subtracting the second number. You may have to provide more pairs of numbers for students to see what the machine is doing.

Make sure they understand that the order of the numbers is important. You can introduce the concept of an ordered pair. Ask how they would key in a sequence to do the same thing as the machine; 2 $\boxed{\times}$ 1st number $\boxed{-}$ 2nd number $\boxed{=}$.

The calculator can be used as a function machine, e.g., two numbers go in, you do some operation or operations, and one number is produced in the display. You can set this up with pairs of numbers using the Basic Overhead Calculator.

For each problem, the order of the numbers is significant; for "12 and 9 go in...," 12 is the first number and 9 is the second number. There are opportunities here for higher-order thinking. For some of the problems, students are given the output number and must supply one of the input numbers. Look at the last problem. This is open ended, any pair of numbers such that 18 is the result of doubling the first number and subtracting the second number.

Extensions

- Provide additional pairs for this "mystery machine."
- If students have worked with addition and multiplication of decimals, extend to using decimals for first and/or second numbers.
- Make up different rules for machines, combining two different operations.
- Have students make up rules for pairs of numbers.

MORE PRODUCT PATHS
See page 40

OBJECTIVES

Students multiply numbers to reach target numbers.

Procedures for Use

Review the directions with students. For each puzzle, students start with the number in the "START" box. Legal moves involve down, over, and up moves. No diagonal moves are permitted. The instruction, "You cannot cross your path." implies that the same number cannot be used more than one time. As students make a path, they multiply the numbers in the boxes. The object is to reach the target product.

Have students work in cooperative groups. Many students will "peck away" hoping to hit the target. Others will use estimation skills. Knowledge of factors and multiples will be used. There are boxes with "0" in them which should assist students in limiting path choices. Students will also use the "1" factors to limit the size of the product. A successful strategy is to factor the target product and try to find a path with the correct factors- but don't tell your students; let them explore.

One strategy students quickly pick up is that the number in the box directly above the target number will be included in the path. Students will learn to not use the larger numbers as factors as the final products will be too large. Remind students how to clear an error. In cooperative groups students will portion out different paths to members of the group to test. Have students discuss their work after all paths are determined. This dialogue is an important part of this activity.

Extensions

- Use the same puzzles to name other target numbers.
- Make additional product paths for the class to solve.
- Have students try to create product paths; start with a 3 x 3 puzzle.

Lesson helper for:

DIVISION SPRINT
See page 41

OBJECTIVES

Students complete division problems in a timed activity.

Procedures for Use

Use after teaching division. Set up the activity as a competition. The objective is to successfully complete the divisions in as short a time as possible.

All the divisors and dividends that are needed are in the number box. Some students will start with the first one and multiply the quotient 27 by numbers in the box hoping to get another number in the box. These students will not have a good elapsed time. Other students will use a combination of estimation skills and number sense to complete the activity.

You may want to have the class do the activity as teams of students. Everyone writes down the start time. Write down finish times as individuals or teams finish. You can deduct time for incorrect answers later.

Extensions

- An extension, although easier than this activity, is to have only a divisor or dividend missing from each example.
- Have students write a report or make a journal entry on the activity.

Lesson helper for:

WACKY WORDS
See page 42

OBJECTIVES

Students engage in problem solving by finding missing numbers in computations.

Procedures for Use

There is a lot of problem solving in this activity. The activity is based on the electronic digits in the display of the TI-108 when viewed upside down resembling certain upper and lower-case letters; 0 = O, 1 = I, 2 = Z, 3 = E, 4 = h, 5 = S, 6 = g, 7 = L, 8 = B, and 9 = G.

Set up the activity by using the artwork on the activity sheet. Have students key in the addition problem, 198 + 119. The display, viewed upside down, yields the word, "LIE." Find other numbers that will yield "words."

The activity involves finding missing numbers so that upside-down displays yield a "word." Look at the first problem. The "word" is "BOSS" and the number that yields the word is 5,508. So, what number added to 2,587 will be 5,508? Students should be able to provide the missing addend by subtracting 2,587 from 5,508.

The number of digits in the missing numbers is provided for each problem. This is important because of the open-ended nature of some of the problems. Look at the sixth problem; the sum of the two numbers must equal 918, and each of the addends must be three-digit numbers. This disallows students giving answers like 917 + 1, 916 + 2, etc. Problem 10 involves critical thinking. There is a range of numbers that will work; remind students that they are looking for a four-digit number divided by a two-digit number.

Extensions

- Create additional words and missing addends or factors for your students to solve.
- Have students develop a vocabulary list of words that are possible.

Lesson helper for:
FAST MATH
See page 43

OBJECTIVES

Students perform whole number operations either by mental math or with calculators.

Procedures for Use

This may be one of the most important activities in this book. One of your major tasks is to teach students to use calculators appropriately. For many computations, it is easier and quicker to use mental math. For other computations, it is much more efficient to use a calculator. You want students to think. You do not want students to do all computations with a calculator. Using activities like FAST MATH will help students to use calculators appropriately. Teach your students to "look before you leap." In other words, before beginning a computation, with paper and pencil or with a calculator, scan the computation to see if a rearrangement of the numbers and application of the properties of operations can result in doing the computation mentally. Mental-math strategies are taught throughout the curriculum; the key is to get students to use these strategies. FAST MATH will help you do this.

Distribute the activity sheet with little or no explanation. Students will ask "Do we have to use the calculator?" Tell them to follow the directions. Keep track of the time it takes students to complete the activity.

Students who are doing every computation with the calculator will not complete the activity within a class period. Others who are using mental math will be finished quickly. There are few computations that require the use of a calculator.

The discussion after the activity is essential. Go over each computation. In some cases, certain ones may not appear to be "mental math."

For example, look at 12. Using the distributive property of multiplication over addition, that is the same as 4 x

10. Similarly, for problem 20., that is the same as 100 x 67. Remember to teach students to "look before you leap."

Teaching mental-math strategies will help students to use calculators appropriately. Activities such as this one will reinforce these important skills.

Extensions

- Repeat this type of activity regularly during the year. The second time around, students will be "on to you" and complete the activity much faster using mental-math skills.
- Do a shorter version of the activity as a warm-up on a regular basis.
- Review mental-math strategies throughout the year.

Lesson helper for:
A PET RIDDLE
See page 44

OBJECTIVES

Students use the features of the TI-108 to simplify expressions and solve a riddle.

Procedures for Use

Use this activity after students have worked with all four operations.

Once students have learned how to press the keys of their calculators, then you want them to be able to do involved computations with their calculators. Few, if any, of these problems can be done mentally by students.

In applications, computations like these will be done with calculators much more efficiently than with pencil and paper.

Review how the TI-108 processes operations. Review how to use the memory keys.

As students find each answer they write it in the space to the right of the problem. Each answer has a letter next to it. They match the letter in the space above the same number in the phrase at the bottom of the activity sheet.

An expression contained within a set of parentheses can be "closed off" by pressing the $=$ key.

Extensions

- Provide additional problems for students to practice using their calculators. Several involved computations together with at least one mental-math problem can serve as an effective warm-up at the beginning of a lesson.
- Try to have the class put together a riddle complete with computations.

Lesson helper for:

SHORT STROKES
See page 45

OBJECTIVES
Students use mental math, estimation, problem-solving skills and calculator skills to reach target numbers.

Procedures for Use
Use this activity after teachng all four operations with whole numbers. It is an effective activity for reviewing the features of the TI-108 and involving students in mental math, estimation, and problem solving.

Set up a competition between individual students or groups of students. There is not enough room on the activity sheet for all the directions so it is important that you review directions with your students.

For each target number, students are restricted to the digit or digits that are given. Using the given digits, and any operation or feature of the TI-108, they can generate numbers and ultimately, lead to the target number. For example, most students will give ③ ➕ ③ ➕ ③ ➖ for the first target number, 9. Don't forget the catch! The object is to reach the target number with the least number of keystrokes. The above sequence uses six keystrokes. Here is a shorter one which uses the automatic constant feature for multiplication: ③ ✖ ➖. That is a total of three keystrokes and hard to beat.

Students must use each of the given digits at least one time in their sequences. They cannot use other digits that are not given. Students cannot use "0" as a placeholder unless it is given.

An important part of this activity is to discuss with the class how "winning" sequences have been generated. You may want to do each target number separately, discuss the winning sequence, i.e., the shortest one, and award points for the first "round," and go on to the next target number. You may be surprised at some of the sequences your students will make as they work through this activity.

Extension
• Provide additional digits to use and target numbers.

Lesson helper for:

EXPONENTS AND PROBLEM SOLVING
See page 46

OBJECTIVES
Students engage in problem solving using a guess-and-check strategy working with exponents.

Procedures for Use
Use this activity anytime after working with whole number multiplication. As an enrichment activity with young students you do not even need to use the term "exponent." Refer to the "little number" which keeps track of the number of times the number is used as a factor.

What you do need to do is teach a generalization before the activity can be used. The TI-108 has an automatic constant for multiplication which allows a shortcut when the same number is to be used as a factor repeatedly. For 2 x 2 or 2^2 press ② ✖ ➖ for a display of 4. For 2 x 2 x 2 or 2^3 press ② ✖ ➖ ➖ for a display of 8. For 2 x 2 x 2 x 2 or 2^4 press ② ✖ ➖ ➖ ➖ for a display of 16. See what is happening? The number of ➖ keys pressed is always one less than the exponent. Similarly, for 5^3 press ⑤ ✖ ➖ ➖ for a display of 125. For 3^6 press ③ ✖ ➖ ➖ ➖ ➖ ➖ for a display of 729. Give students ample practice so they understand the generalization.

Once they have calculated many powers of numbers, distribute the activity sheet. Students will want to know what to do-tell them to guess! Guess and check is an excellent problem-solving strategy. If the guess results in an answer too large, try a smaller number. If too small, try a larger number. By repeated trials, students will hone in on the correct number.

As students explore, insights will be made; e.g., odd and even numbers raised to odd or even exponents, the units digit of answers and how that limits the choice of base numbers. Good opportunities here for explorations! Discuss with students the various processes used in solving the problems.

Extensions
• Make a game out of the activity by keeping track of the number of guesses it takes to find the base number. Student estimation skills seem to improve when there is competition involved!
• Have students prepare problems. Check their work before they present them to the class.

Lesson helper for:

NUMBER PYRAMIDS
See page 47

OBJECTIVES
Students complete pyramid puzzles by finding missing addends and factors.

Procedures for Use
Use this activity after teaching all four operations with decimals.

Explain the activity sheet to students. Numbers in each row of the pyramids are obtained by operating on the two numbers in the row directly below them. For the first two pyramids, students have to determine which operation is being used. For the first one, 13.4 + 7.12 = 20.52; thus, addition must be used to complete the puzzle. Students will use subtraction to find the missing number in the bottom row and addition to find the missing number in the top row. The key to completing the first two pyramids is to determine the operation. Do not tell students the operation being used; let them discover what is happening.

Similarly, for the second pyramid, 3.5 x 4.4 = 15.4, so multiplication will be used throughout the pyramid. Students work up and down through the pyramid using multiplication and division.

There is no completed "problem" within the next three pyramids, so students are given the operation to use. Again, students will use addition and subtraction, and multiplication and division to complete the pyramids. Make sure students check their work; all numbers in the rows must be sums or products of the numbers immediately below them.

Discuss how students found the missing numbers.

Extensions

- Have students help you make up new addition and multiplication pyramids.
- Give students a challenge for the addition pyramids. Ask them to add a new bottom row; what numbers will go in the rows?

Lesson helper for:
ANOTHER TARGET TOSS
See page 48

OBJECTIVES

Students use multiplication and division of decimals to determine factors of target numbers.

Procedures for Use

Use this after students have worked with multiplication and division of decimals.

You have to use your imagination here. Your students will have no trouble using their imaginations! Actually, you could make a game board, tape it to the chalkboard, and have students throw real bean bags at the board. The big difference is that with this activity it is assumed that all bean bags hit a number. Your students will not be that accurate. First check with your principal.

This embodies the type of activity for which the calculator is an excellent aid. Set up the game. As bean bags are "thrown" and hit numbers, the numbers are multiplied. Students are given the scores (products) and must determine which numbers are hit. Make sure students understand that they need to get the product with the correct number of bean bags. In some cases, they may get the right product but with the incorrect number of bags thrown. They will ask if you can hit the same number more than once. Let them discover that you must in some of the problems.

For three throws (problems 1., 2. and 6.), many students will use mental math. For the other throws, some students will multiply numbers randomly attempting to hit the score. Other students will use division, trying to "break down" the number into factors that match the numbers on the board. Students have many opportunities here to explore decimal computations using their calculator. There is a lot of math here!

Extensions

- Use other decimals and make up more game boards.
- Use more than 4 numbers to a board.
- Have students write about the activity. How did they feel in searching for the numbers?

Lesson helper for:
FIND THE OPERATIONS
See page 49

OBJECTIVES

Students find missing operations in key sequences.

Students use mental math and estimation skills.

Procedures for Use

Use this activity after working with decimals.

This is one of those calculator activities which reinforces use of mental math and estimation skills. Each sequence has one or two operations missing; students have to determine the correct operations and the correct order of the operations. Accept answers as they are found. Tell your students you are trying to set a world's record for finishing FIND THE OPERATIONS. You may be surprised how quickly the missing operations are found.

Some of the sequences involve use of the constant capability of the TI-108. For example, [4] [x] [=] [=] [=] yields a display of 256 (4 x 4 x 4 x 4).

Extensions

- Provide additional sequences which include more operations.
- Use this idea as a source of warm-ups for other lessons.

Lesson helper for:

DECIMAL PATTERNS
See page 50

OBJECTIVES

Students use mental math and higher-order thinking skills to find missing numbers in patterns involving decimals.

Procedures for Use

This activity can be used anytime after students work with all four operations with decimals. Review the directions to an earlier activity, SEARCHING FOR PATTERNS.

To get from one number to the next one, students must apply the same "rule." Make sure students understand that the same operation or operations must be performed each time to get to the next number. Students cannot change the "rule" in the middle of a pattern.

Finding missing numbers in patterns involving decimals provides students with an opportunity to explore with their TI-108s.

Have students explain their answers. This is an opportunity for students to communicate their thinking. Answers are not unique in that while one student will say "multiply by 0.5," another will say "divide by 2." They are both correct.

Extensions

- Show students how to use the features of the TI-108 to generate numbers in some of the patterns; e.g., for pattern 1., press: $\boxed{1}\ \boxed{+}\ \boxed{\cdot}\ \boxed{0}\ \boxed{7}\ \boxed{=}\ \boxed{=}\ \boxed{=}\ \boxed{=}\ \boxed{=}\ \boxed{=}$.
- Have students generate patterns for the class to guess the "rule."

Lesson helper for:

SHOPPING FOR FRUIT AND VEGGIES
See page 51

OBJECTIVES

Students determine total costs of orders at a veggie and fruit cart...

Procedures for Use

This is a busy looking activity sheet but just the type of activity for which the TI-108 was designed. Use this activity after students have learned to use all the features of the TI-108 and have covered multiplication and problems involving money.

Review the directions with your class. Make sure they understand the price structure for the various items; some

items are sold by the pound, each, and several for a certain amount. Review the use of the symbol for "pound." Though it is common to use the symbol "lbs." for the plural of pound, most advertisements will use "lb." No operations with fractions are involved; assume that lettuce comes in nice pound bunches. Explain the cost of 6 oranges. If a customer only wants 6 oranges, the cost would be half of $1.99, rounded up to $1.

Have some fun with your class and bring in from home some of the vegetables and fruits used in the activity. Students in some areas of the country may not be familiar with all the different vegetables and fruits used.

Be sure to allow time for students to discuss how they did their work.

Extensions

- Have students determine the correct change for each order by telling them how much money is given to the clerk for each order. For example, for order #1, if the clerk is given a $20 bill, how much change is due?
- Have students make up additional orders.
- Have students bring in newspaper advertisements from the food section of the local newspaper. Create additional activities, involving food purchases.
- Another type of extension involves giving students a total cost and having them try to determine what was purchased.

Lesson helper for:

DECIMAL MAZE
See page 52

OBJECTIVES

Students perform operations with decimals in a puzzle format.

Procedures for Use

Use after teaching all four operations with decimals.

Explain the activity to your students. They need to find a path from the "START" box to the "FINISH" box. The catch is to find a pattern of numbers that will lead them from "START" to "FINISH," something like 2, 4, 6, 8, etc. or 5, 10, 15, 20, etc. So, once they do several problems and see a pattern developing, they do not have to do all the problems, only those that are on their possible pattern path. Obviously, students could do all twenty-eight problems then find the pattern. The object is to find the pattern doing the least number of problems. Students who use mental math searching for a pattern will complete the activity much faster doing less problems.

Paths can go down and across, left or right. Paths cannot go up or on a diagonal. Students may follow what appears to be a pattern only to go up a "blind alley." They then have to backtrack and start anew. Some students will immediately recognize that box 1. and box 28. will be part of the path, so the number 2 starts the pattern and the number 46 is the end of the pattern.

Many of the problems will be done by students using mental math and this should be encouraged.

Extensions

- Provide additional puzzles for students to practice operations with decimals.
- Survey students to determine the number of problems completed before the pattern and path were found.

Lesson helper for:
DECIMAL DETECTIVE
See page 53

OBJECTIVES

Students use clues about numbers to solve word "mysteries."

Procedure for Use

Use this activity after students have worked with all four operations with decimals. Have them work in groups. Communication skills are important in this activity. Students read clues about "mystery numbers" and then try to identify the numbers.

Set up the activity by doing the first one together. This is a missing addend problem. "What number added to 14.7 will give you a sum of 52.6?" Hopefully, students won't add up from 14.7 to get to 52.6, but will subtract 14.7 from 52.6. If students have trouble with this, use a simpler problem, such as "If you add me to 5, the sum is 9. Who am I?" Similar techniques with the other problems will help students through the activity. Working backwards and using relationships between addition and subtraction, and multiplication and division are successful strategies to use. Review the difference in terminology like "multiply and then add" and "add and then multiply" and how the TI-108 processes operations.

Have students check their work by replacing the word "me" with the answer.

Extensions

- Have students create mystery stories involving decimal numbers. Use students as "actors" to read the stories to the class to solve.
- Develop a bulletin board activity using the students' stories.

Lesson helper for:
FIND THE MATCHES
See page 54

OBJECTIVES

Students use mental math, number sense, and basic skills to match expressions.

Procedure for Use

Use this activity after teaching operations with fractions, decimals, and percents.

This is one of those calculator activities which reinforces mental math. You want to use this as a timed activity. Prior to distributing the activity sheet, explain to the class that the objective is to find five matches as quickly as possible.

In the grid there are 24 expressions, twelve pairs of matching ones. Explain to students that they only have to find five of the matching pairs. Build up the activity as a game. "Ready, get set, go!" Students list their matches on the sheet. To keep track of the simplified expressions, instruct students to put the "answers" in the boxes; e.g., for A., students should write a "490" in the "A." box. Then they would search for another "490." Your students will not necessarily do the first one; they will jump around looking for the "easier" computations. You can either check individual students' matches as they complete the activity or wait till most of the class is finished. Record the time lapse for students on their papers.

Students who complete the activity successfully in the shortest time will use mental math and number sense. Other students who rely on the calculator will take the longest to complete the sheet. Make sure they understand that they do not have to do all 24 problems, but only find five matches. It would be rare for someone to do just ten problems to find the five matches.

Have students discuss the activity and explain the process they used to find their five matches. Insights into students' thinking will emerge. Use this timed format many times during the school year. It is an excellent way for students to learn the appropriate use of calculators.

Extensions

- Extend the discussion. "Who used mental math to find matches?" "Which ones?" You want students to see that, in many cases, it is quicker to use mental math rather than the calculator.
- For each of the twelve matches, have students create additional matches; e.g., A. is the same as 490. Have students find additional names for 490 using two operations, decimals, etc.

Lesson helper for:
MORE SHORT STROKES
See page 55

OBJECTIVES
Students use mental math, estimation, problem-solving skills and calculator skills to reach target numbers.

Procedure for Use
Use this activity after teaching all four operations with whole numbers and decimals. It is an effective activity for reviewing the features of the TI-108 and involving students in mental math, estimation, and problem solving. You may want to review an earlier activity, SHORT STROKES.

For each target number, students are restricted to the digit or digits that are given. Some of the problems also give a decimal point key which must be used at least once. Using the given digits, and any operation or feature of the TI-108, they can generate numbers and ultimately, lead to the target number. The object is to reach the target number with the least number of keystrokes.

Students must use each of the given digits at least one time in their sequences. They cannot use other digits that are not given. Students cannot use "0" as a place-holder unless it is given. If a target number is a decimal number and no decimal point is given, division must be used to generate decimals.

Extension
- Provide additional digits to use and target numbers.

Lesson helper for:
COLUMN MATH
See page 56

OBJECTIVES
Students use various problem-solving strategies to complete equations.

Procedure for Use
Use this activity after teaching all operations with decimals and fractions.

Provide students with directions before they start on the activity. The first number missing in each equation will come from Column I, the second number from Column II. Each number is to be used only one time; when finished, all numbers will be used.

This activity combines many problem-solving strategies. Students will use trial and error to find missing numbers.

Some students will use estimation and mental math. Others may work backwards, working with the right side of each equation and experimenting with numbers in Column II and the inverse operation to find a number from Column I.

A successful strategy is to first do the equations which involve addition and subtraction. The pairs of numbers for these equations can be found using estimation and mental math. Once these pairs are found, students can then work on each of the other equations.

It is recommended that students use a pencil with an eraser for this activity. There will be "blind alleys" followed. Students should check off numbers as they are used or they will not be able to keep track of what numbers have been used.

Discuss methods used by your students after the activity is completed. You may be surprised at the processes your students used.

Extension
- Have students write about the activity including the methods they used to find the missing numbers.

Lesson helper for:
PERCENT MAZE
See page 57

OBJECTIVES
Students find percents of numbers in a puzzle format.

Procedure for Use
Use after teaching finding percents of numbers, including decimal numbers.

Explain the activity to your students. They need to find a path from the "START" box to the "FINISH" box. The catch is to find a pattern of numbers that will lead them from "START" to "FINISH," something like 2, 4, 6, 8, etc. or 5, 10, 15, 20, etc. So, once they do several problems and see a pattern developing, they do not have to do all the problems, only those that are on their possible pattern path. Obviously, students could do all twenty-eight problems then find the pattern. The object is to find the pattern doing the least number of problems. Students who use mental math searching for a pattern will complete the activity much faster doing less problems.

Paths can go down and across, left or right. Paths cannot go up or on a diagonal. Students may follow what appears to be a pattern only to go up a "blind alley." They then have to backtrack and start anew. Some students will immediately recognize that box 1. and box 28. will be part of the path, so the number 4 starts the pattern and the number 48 is the end of the pattern.

Many of the problems will be done by students using mental math and this should be encouraged. Review how to find a percent of a number using the TI-108.

Extensions

- Provide additional puzzles to practice finding percents of numbers.
- Survey students to determine the number of problems completed before the pattern and path were found.

Lesson helper for:
BOB'S BIKE BARN
See page 58

OBJECTIVES

Students solve problems involving markup and discount.

Procedure for Use

Use this activity after teaching percent, including markup and discount applications.

Review use of the %. With the TI-108, the base number in a percent problem is first keyed in. For 25% of 60, key in 6 0 x 2 5 % for a display of 15.

The TI-108 is set up to provide shortcuts for markup and discount. For an item with a ticket price of $60 and discounted 25%, key in 6 0 − 2 5 % for a display of 45. This sequence gives the sale price; you do not get to see the cash discount. Another way of doing the same problem is to use the memory keys. Key in 6 0 M+ x 2 5 % M− MRC. Using the memory keys, you get to see the cash discount, ($15) in the display before it is subtracted from the original price in the memory. Notice after 60 is put in memory it is not necessary to key it in again, it is still in the display. Markup would be done similarly.

Markup and discount problems are referred to as two-step problems with paper and pencil. Here is a one-step problem that is taught usually as an enrichment topic. If the $60 item is discounted 25%, then the sale price represents 75% of the original price. Key in 6 0 x 7 5 % for the display of 45.

Discuss the psychology of pricing with students; it sounds cheaper to ticket an item at $34.99 than at $35. Also, despite the usual rounding rules, stores will always round up if part of a penny is owed.

Extensions

- No sales tax was included in the activity because it differs from state to state. Include a sales tax, if applicable locally, and have students compute total cost including tax.

- Add items to the store's specials and make up new problems.
- Use newspaper advertisements to provide practice with markup and discount.

Lesson helper for:
MORE FAST MATH
See page 59

OBJECTIVES

Students perform computations with decimals either by mental math or with calculators.

Procedure for Use

Review the lesson helper for FAST MATH. This type of activity is essential in teaching students to use calculators appropriately.

Distribute the activity sheet with little or no explanation. Students will ask "Do we have to use the calculator?" Tell them to follow the directions. Keep track of the time it takes students to complete the activity. Students who are doing every computation with the calculator will not complete the activity within a class period. Others who are using mental math will be finished quickly. There are few computations that require the use of a calculator.

Remember to teach students to "look before you leap." Teaching mental-math strategies will help students to use calculators appropriately. Activities such as this one will reinforce these important skills.

Extensions

- Repeat this type of activity regularly during the year. With repeated use, students will be "on to you" and complete the activity much faster using mental-math skills.
- Do a shorter version of the activity as a warm-up on a regular basis.
- Review mental-math strategies throughout the year.

Lesson helper for:
CHANGE THE SIGNS
See page 60

OBJECTIVES

Students add integers to find missing numbers in calculator sequences.

Procedure for Use

Integers are introduced in the middle grades. Use this activity after students have worked with addition of integers.

Review the need for the set of integers-profit, loss; elevation above and below sea level; yards gained and lost in football; etc. Review how to display a negative number. For –4, press 4 $+/-$. Notice that the change sign key is pressed after the digit 4. Whenever the change sign key is pressed, the display will show the additive inverse or opposite of the number that was in the display. Look at the display. The negative sign is to the extreme left of the display. It is a non-floating negative sign; i.e., it does not float to a position immediately in front of the digits in a number. Make sure students understand how the TI-108 displays negative numbers.

In this activity, students supply missing numbers in addition sequences involving integers. The last two problems are open-ended.

Extensions

- Once students understand how to add integers, use larger positive integers and smaller negative integers.
- Have students provide a context for each of the sequences; e.g., for the first one, "You earn $8 and pay a bill of $3. How much do you have left?"
- Prepare a set of flash cards having positive and negative integers on them. Use single digit integers; –8, 6, 5, –3, 2, –1, and so on. Hold two of them up for the students to add as quickly as possible. The purpose of this type of activity is to reinforce to your students that in certain cases, mental math is much quicker than the use of the calculator.

Lesson helper for:

EXPONENT EXPLORATIONS
See page 61

OBJECTIVES

Students solve equations using a guess-and check strategy working with exponents.

Procedure for Use

Review the lesson helper for EXPONENTS AND PROBLEM SOLVING.

If you used the above activity, you have taught a generalization for working with exponents using the TI-108. It has an automatic constant for multiplication which allows a shortcut when the same number is to be used as a factor repeatedly. For 2 x 2 or 2^2 press 2 $\times$ $=$ for a display of 4. For 2 x 2 x 2 or 2^3 press 2 $\times$ $=$ $=$ for a display of 8. For 2 x 2 x 2 or 2^4 press 2 $\times$ $=$ $=$ $=$ for a display of 16. See what is happening? The number of $=$ keys pressed is always one less than the exponent. Review use of the generalization.

Distribute the activities sheet. "Let's see. For the first equation, I'm looking for a number that when 1 is added to the number multiplied by itself, the result is 26. So the number when multiplied by itself is 25. The number is 5." This is the kind of thinking students use to solve the equations. Much of the work is using mental math to arrive at a possible answer. Students then use their TI-108s to check their reasoning .

Activities such as this one involve the learning of good pre-algebra skills. Discuss with students the various processes used in solving the equations.

Extensions

- Provide more difficult equations for students to solve.
- Have students prepare problems. Check their work before they present them to the class.

Lesson helper for:

MATCH THE COLUMNS
See page 62

OBJECTIVES

Students use the square root key on the TI-108 calculator.

Procedure for Use

When students first use the square root key on the TI-108, they may be confused. Pressing the square root key calculates the square root of whatever is in the display, e.g., to find the square root of 25, press 2 5 $\sqrt{}$. The display will read 5. To be precise, the display shows the positive square root of 25, –5 x –5 also equals 25. This differs from a standard expression written with pencil and paper where the square root symbol is written first.

This activity reinforces students' understanding of the relationship between key sequences and standard expressions involving square roots.

Show students the difference between keying in the square root of a sum and the sum of square roots; e.g., $\sqrt{9+16} = 5$ and $\sqrt{9} + \sqrt{16} = 7$. Show students how to calculate the square root of a sum by closing off the sum through use of the $=$ key; e.g., to find $\sqrt{9+16}$, press 9 $+$ 1 6 $=$ $\sqrt{}$. Many of the matches will be found by using mental math; encourage students' use of mental math strategies.

Extensions

- Provide additional expressions with more difficult computations.
- Provide students with standard expressions and have them provide you with appropriate key sequences.

Lesson helper for:

RIGHT TRIANGLE STUFF
See page 63

OBJECTIVES

Students find lengths of right triangles using the Pythagorean Theorem.

Procedure for Use

At the middle school level, the Pythagorean Theorem is an important component of the geometry strand. Once students have been taught the relationship between the hypotenuse and the other two sides of a right triangle, you want to provide them with applications using the Theorem. With access to calculators, students can easily handle non-integer lengths of sides.

Allow students to devise their own methods of finding missing lengths of right triangles. Here are two efficient sequences. To find the hypotenuse (h) of a right triangle using the TI-108, given the lengths of sides a and b, press a [X] [=] [M+] b [X] [=] [M+] [MRC] [√]. The display will read h. To find one of the other sides; e.g., b, press h [X] [=] [M+] a [X] [=] [M−] [MRC] [√]. The display will yield b. Pressing the [=] key following each of the multiplications in the above sequences is not necessary.

Extensions

- Have individual students create additional examples.
- Provide students with the following process question: if a, b, c is a Pythagorean triple, what about ka, kb, kc where k > 0? For example, 3, 4, 5 is a Pythagorean triple. If k = 5, is 15, 20, 25 a Pythagorean triple?

Lesson helper for:

SHORT STROKES & SQUARE ROOTS
See page 64

OBJECTIVES

Students use mental math, estimation, problem-solving skills and calculator skills to reach target numbers.

Procedure for Use

This activity is similar to other short-stroke activities contained in this book but provides additional practice with using the square root key. For each target number, students are restricted to the digit or digits that are given. Using the given digits, and any operation or feature of the TI-108 with at least one use of the square root key, they can generate numbers and ultimately, lead to the target number. The object is to reach the target number with the least number of keystrokes.

Students must use each of the given digits at least one time in their sequences. They cannot use other digits that are not given. Students cannot use "0" as a placeholder unless it is given. The decimal point or the operation of division can be used to generate decimal numbers.

An important part of this activity is to discuss with the class how "winning" sequences have been generated. You may want to do each target number separately, discuss the winning sequence, i.e., the shortest one, and award points for the first "round," and go on to the next target number. You may be surprised at some of the sequences your students will make as they work through this activity.

Extensions

- Provide additional digits to use and target numbers.
- Have students generate additional "rounds" for the rest of the class to solve.

Lesson helper for:

CHEERLEADER MATH
See page 65

OBJECTIVES

Students use knowledge of order of operations and use of parenthesis keys to complete equations.

Procedure for Use

Tell students that because they are sad that this is the last activity, this one contains a cheer. This last activity ties together most of the calculator and mathematics skills that have been covered in this book. It would be rare indeed to do any of the equations using mental math; their ability to use their TI-108s will become apparent.

Because the TI-108 processes operations from left to right, students need to effectively use the memory keys to complete the equations. Review order of operations, properties of operations, and other calculator skills before using the activity.

Explain the directions to the class. As they complete each equation, the number is matched with a letter. Students then find the same number under the blanks in the cheer below and fill in the blank with the matching letter. When all equations are completed and letters placed in the blanks, students will find the missing word in the cheer.

Extensions

- Have students discuss methods used to complete the equations. This discussion will provide insights into student thinking processes.
- Provide additional practice using order of operations and parentheses.